THE LITTLE BOOK OF
SHELLS
GEMS OF NATURE

M. G. Harasewych is an Emeritus Curator in the Department of Invertebrate Zoology at the National Museum of Natural History, Smithsonian Institution in Washington, D.C., which houses one of the world's largest mollusk collections. He has discovered a variety of new species, written widely for journals and periodicals, and authored *Shells: Jewels from the Sea*.

Fabio Moretzsohn is a Professional Assistant Professor in the Department of Life Sciences, Texas A&M University-Corpus Christi. He is one of the authors of the *Encyclopedia of Texas Seashells*.

First published in the UK in 2020 by
Ivy Press
An imprint of The Quarto Group
The Old Brewery, 6 Blundell Street
London N7 9BH, United Kingdom
T (0)20 7700 6700
www.QuartoKnows.com

Material in this book was first published in 2010 in *The Book of Shells*

British Library Cataloguing-in-Publication Data
A catalogue record for this book is available from
the British Library

ISBN: 978-0-7112-5269-1

This book was designed and produced by
Ivy Press
58 West Street, Brighton BN1 2RA, UK

Publisher David Breuer
Editorial Director Tom Kitch
Art Director James Lawrence
Commissioning Editors Kate Shanahan, Natalia Price-Cabrera
Project Editor Joanna Bentley
Designer Ginny Zeal
Additional Research Steve Luck, Colin Slater
Map Artwork Richard Peters

Printed in China

10 9 8 7 6 5 4 3 2 1

MIX
Paper from
responsible sources
FSC® C008047

THE LITTLE BOOK OF
SHELLS
GEMS OF NATURE

M. G. HARASEWYCH
& FABIO MORETZSOHN

IVY PRESS

CONTENTS

INTRODUCTION

Anyone who has been to the seaside or the shore of a lake or river, or who has walked through the woods or a garden has probably seen and picked up a few shells. Few, however, will have paused to consider the extraordinary variety of forms into which mollusks mold their shells, each the product of a long evolutionary history and each adapted to a particular habitat.

Shells are the external skeletons of mollusks. Like ancient volumes or tablets, they record the history of the animals that made them. Shells archive every aspect of the animal's life, from its early larval stage through the years, decades, or, in some cases, a century or more of life. If fossilized, they may preserve this information for hundreds of millions of years.

A well preserved larval shell may tell us whether the animal was brooded or hatched from an egg capsule as a crawling juvenile, or if it spent time in the plankton before metamorphosing into a small version of an adult. All mollusks increase the size of their shells by adding incrementally to their edges; to the margins of shell plates in chitons, to valve edges in bivalves, to apertural margins in scaphopods, gastropods, and cephalopods. Much like tree rings, these sequential layers chronicle the life of the mollusk, sometimes in intricate detail. Some intertidal bivalves, for example, add shell material when the tide is in, but resorb shell when the tide is out, producing a new, recognizable layer with each tidal cycle.

Some shells grow slowly and regularly, others quickly and episodically, producing large sections often demarcated by varices (thickening along the lip of a shell). Most mollusks grow rapidly and in a regular pattern until they reach adulthood, when energy is redirected from growth to reproduction. Some continue to grow in the same general pattern, although much more slowly. Others, such as cowries, have terminal growth, altering the shape of their shell irrevocably in a way that precludes further growth. These adults differ dramatically in appearance from juveniles. They may continue to thicken their shells to become heavier, but not much larger.

Many of the most conspicuous attributes of a shell are inherited, and indicate its genealogy. The distinctive shapes of scallops, spider conchs, or chambered nautiluses clearly identify them as members of their respective classes, families, and genera. Other features, such as a flattened limpet shape, may be adaptations to particular habitats that occur independently in many different lineages.

More subtle features of shape and condition provide a wealth of information about the species or even the individual specimen. The presence of large varices and spines indicate that the animals live on hard substrates, while smooth, tapered, elongated shells are characteristic of animals that burrow into sand or mud. Similarly, delicate, frilly spines that remain unbroken reveal a calm, subtidal habitat, while worn or eroded shells are indicators of exposure to waves. Repaired shell breaks or incomplete boreholes bear witness to attacks by predators, while traces of encrusting organisms, boring sponges, and symbionts all add information about the life and times of the animal that produced the shell.

It is second nature to us to admire the delicate shape, color, and beauty of a perfect specimen. Taking the time to "read" each shell as an autobiography of the animal that produced it is often just as rewarding.

Although all seashells are made by mollusks, not all mollusks make shells. Of those mollusks that do make shells, the majority live in the seas and oceans of the world, from the tropics to the poles, from above the high tide line, where only wave spray reaches, to the bottoms of ocean trenches. While mollusks originated and diversified in the oceans, a sizeable proportion of species now live on land or in fresh water, the results of numerous independent colonizations of these habitats.

In terms of the number of living species, mollusks are the most diverse animals in the oceans. While the best known and most familiar mollusks tend to be the larger, more conspicuous species, molluscan diversity is dominated by small animals. A study of the shelled mollusks from a site in New Caledonia revealed a range in sizes from $\frac{1}{64}$ in (0.4 mm) to 18 in (450 mm), with an average size of $\frac{2}{3}$ in (17 mm). On average, almost 85 percent of the species were less than 2 in (50 mm), and most are far smaller.

When perusing the shells depicted in this book, it is informative to consider that they represent but a fraction of known species of mollusks, and that a proportional sampling of the phylum would have produced a work dominated by tiny snails. Many of the major lineages of shelled mollusks living in the sea are represented here, and they are arranged according to current understanding of the branching patterns of their evolutionary history.

WHAT IS A MOLLUSK?

Mollusks are among the oldest and most diverse groups of animals on the planet. Like all taxa, they are defined by their genealogy. That is to say, they have a common ancestor from which all members of the phylum Mollusca, living and extinct, are descended.

Early mollusks

The earliest mollusks were small ($\frac{1}{25}$–$\frac{1}{12}$ in/1–2 mm), marine, bilaterally symmetrical animals, with an anterior head, a ventral foot, and a posterior mantle cavity that contained paired gills, sensory organs called osphradia, openings of the genital and excretory organs, and the anus. The head contained a mouth with a radula, a ribbonlike feeding structure unique to mollusks that is like a flexible rasp. The foot was an elongated structure used for locomotion, and the visceral mass, situated above the foot, contained the major organ systems, including the heart, kidneys, digestive glands, and gonads. The nervous system consisted of three pairs of ganglia, one for each body region (the head, foot, and viscera). A cuticle covering the body secreted calcareous spicules or scales.

Over the course of geological time, the descendants of this common ancestor diversified and differentiated, giving rise to multiple branches, each with distinctive features and adaptations. Many of the most basal of these branches, the classes within the phylum Mollusca, diverged during the Cambrian period. Some, such as the Gastropoda, Bivalvia, and Cephalopoda, underwent significant anatomical changes, producing combinations of features that enabled rapid exploitation of new environments. Other classes (among them the Polyplacophora, Monoplacophora,

Scaphopoda) retained their basic anatomical organization; they persist to the present day, little modified and with comparatively low diversity. Mollusks are so ancient and diverse that there are few diagnostic characters that are both unique to Mollusca and ubiquitous to all its classes.

Chitons

The chitons (Class Polyplacophora) have elongated, flattened, bilaterally symmetrical bodies covered by a shell of eight overlapping transverse plates that are surrounded by a cuticularized girdle (muscular band). The foot is long and muscular, and flanked on both sides and by a long mantle cavity that contains multiple pairs of gills (from 6 to 88). The head is reduced, lacking eyes and tentacles. Light-sensing cells that are unique to chitons pass through tiny canals in the shell plates. All chitons live in the ocean, most on rocky bottoms in fairly shallow water where they graze on algae and sponges.

Gastroverms

Gastroverms (Class Monoplacophora) are relatively small ($\frac{1}{36}$–$1\frac{1}{2}$ in/ 0.7–37 mm), ovate, bilaterally symmetrical mollusks that have a single, conical, limpetlike shell with eight pairs of serially repeated muscle scars. They were thought to be extinct, but more than thirty living species have been discovered since 1957, nearly all from deepsea habitats (571–21,289 ft/174–6,489 m), where they inhabit muddy, rocky, or gravelly bottoms. All feed on organic matter and on small animals in the sediment.

Bivalves

Bivalves (Class Bivalvia) are the second largest class of mollusks. They have a bilaterally symmetrical body that is completely enclosed in a shell consisting of two valves (left and right) that are connected by an elastic ligament. The head is reduced, and the radula is absent. Most bivalves have a capacious mantle cavity that accommodates large gills. In addition to being respiratory organs, they filter food particles from the water. Some primitive forms feed directly on the organic matter in fine sediments, a few specialized groups derive nutrition from symbiotic algae or bacteria, while others capture and consume small crustaceans and worms in the deep sea. Most bivalves burrow in sand or mud, some in wood, clay, or coral. Some attach to hard substrates with threadlike strands (byssus), others by cementing one of their valves.

Scaphopods

Scaphopods (Class Scaphopoda) comprise a small group of about 900 living species. They have tall, bilaterally symmetrical bodies completely contained in a long, curved, tapering tubular shell that is open at both ends. Scaphopods lack eyes and gills. They burrow in soft bottoms using a foot that emerges from the larger opening. The smaller opening remains near the surface of the sediment. Scaphopods feed on microscopic organisms in the sediment, which they capture with thin, threadlike tentacles called captacula.

Gastropods

Gastropods or snails (Class Gastropoda) comprise the largest class of mollusks. During their larval stage, all gastropods undergo torsion, a process that twists the animal until the formerly posterior mantle cavity is rotated to a position over the head, resulting in an asymmetrical animal with a single coiled shell. Snail shells assume a variety of forms, ranging from microscopic ($1/75$ in/0.3 mm) to enormous (39 in/1 m). The shell of a snail may be external, internal, or entirely absent. Like bivalves, snails inhabit all marine and freshwater habitats. Unlike any other mollusks, some snails developed lungs and have also colonized land environments ranging from forests to mountains to deserts. Snails may be herbivores, carnivores, parasites, filter feeders, detritivores, or even chemoautotrophs.

Cephalopods

The earliest cephalopods (Class Cephalopoda) had external shells, with chambers that were interconnected by a tube that allowed them to become gas-filled and buoyant. During the course of their evolution, the vast majority of cephalopods have lost an external shell. Some, including cuttlefish and squid have internal shells that have been reduced to various degrees; octopuses lack any shell at all.

Cephalopods inhabit all oceans at all depths. Many live in shallow coastal areas, while others are pelagic, spending their lives swimming or drifting through the open ocean at great distances from surface, shore, or bottom. Cephalopods range from 1 in (25 mm) to more than 46 ft (14 m) in length, and include both the Giant Squid and the even larger Colossal Squid, the largest known invertebrate. All are predatory, with the head and mouth surrounded by muscular, sucker-bearing tentacles that capture prey, which is then eaten with a parrotlike beak and radular teeth.

WHAT IS A SHELL?

As broadly defined, a shell is a hard outer covering that encases certain organisms, usually for the purpose of protecting them from the environment. Many organisms, ranging from microscopic foraminifera to turtles, produce shells using a variety of materials.

How a shell forms

External shells composed of calcium carbonate are secreted by many invertebrate phyla, among them Cnidaria (corals), Arthropoda (crabs and barnacles), Echinodermata (sea urchins), Brachiopoda (lamp shells), and Bryozoa (moss animals), yet the term "shell" or, more specifically "seashell" almost inevitably conjures the image of the calcified external skeleton of a mollusk.

The shell is secreted by the mantle (or pallium), a specialized tissue that is present in every mollusk. One section produces a thin layer of a protein called conchiolin. Other cells secrete a fluid into the narrow space between the animal's tissues and the conchiolin layer. Calcium carbonate crystallizes from the fluid onto the inner surface of the conchiolin, producing a continuously mineralized shell. The shells of all mollusks are secreted outside the animal's tissues.

In all mollusks, shell growth occurs through the addition of new bands of conchiolin along the existing edges of the shell, followed by crystallization of calcium carbonate onto this matrix. Shells can be made thicker by the successive secretion of conchiolin matrix and calcium carbonate to produce additional internal layers.

Parts of a Bivalve

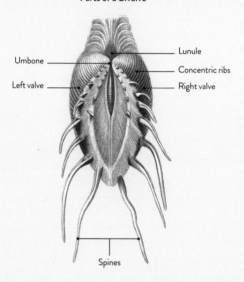

Umbone

Left valve

Lunule

Concentric ribs

Right valve

Spines

Bivalves

The shells of bivalves consist of two separate valves. The tiny larva of a bivalve produces a single, uncalcified, caplike shell, called a pellicle. As the larva grows, it is gradually enveloped by two mantle lobes, each developing a separate center of calcification—the dissoconchs, the parts of the shell produced after the larva metamorphoses, assume the features and proportions of the adult bivalve.

Most bivalves are composed of two valves that are mirror images of each other. The shell usually consists of three layers: an outer periostracum, which may be quite thick in some species, and outer and inner shell layers. The outer layer forms surface details such as scales or spines. In some bivalves, the shells have become reduced; in others, they have become incorporated into large, cylindrical tubes.

Scaphopod External Shell Features

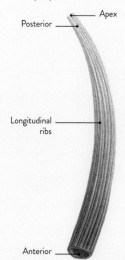

Posterior — Apex

Longitudinal ribs

Anterior

Chiton External Shell Features

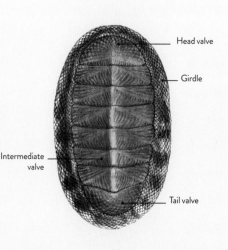

Head valve

Girdle

Intermediate valve

Tail valve

Scaphopods

The tubular shell of scaphopods starts as a small, caplike shell in the larva. During development, the edges expand to surround the larva and fuse along the opposite side to form a tube. After metamorphosis, growth occurs through the addition of shell to the circular edge of the anterior opening, producing a shell consisting of a periostracum and two to four layers of aragonite, a crystalline form of calcium carbonate. As the shell grows, the length and anterior diameter increase and the inner walls thicken. The posterior opening is maintained at an appropriate diameter by the mantle, which dissolves constricting portions of the shell.

Chitons

The shells of chitons are secreted as eight separate plates, and include a head valve, six intermediate valves, and a tail valve. Each valve is composed of four separate layers. The outermost layer is the periostracum; beneath it is the tegmentum; then comes the articulamentum, the thickest and hardest of the layers; the innermost layer is the hypostracum, which is composed of columnar crystals. The valves are held together by muscles and a cuticular girdle that fits between the tegmentum and articulamentum. Depending on the species, the girdle may be covered by proteinaceous hairs, or calcareous spines, granules, or scales.

Gastropod External Shell Features

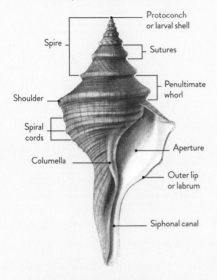

Protoconch
or larval shell

Spire

Sutures

Penultimate
whorl

Shoulder

Spiral
cords

Columella

Aperture

Outer lip
or labrum

Siphonal canal

Cephalopod External Shell Features

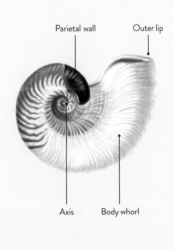

Parietal wall

Outer lip

Axis

Body whorl

Gastropods and cephalopods

The shells of gastropods and cephalopods all begin as simple, cap-shaped shells formed by the larvae of these mollusks. Growth occurs by incremental addition to the roughly circular rim to produce a conical shell. In extinct ancestral cephalopods, the caplike larval shells continued to grow into long, narrow, conical tubes. The animals remained near the base of the cone, and periodically sealed off the upper portions of the cone with partitions (septa). The few surviving species of *Nautilus* are the only cephalopods living today that still have external shells. In all other living cephalopods, the shell has become internal, greatly reduced, or is absent.

Gastropods also begin life with caplike larval shells. However, their larvae undergo torsion, a 180-degree twisting of the body that produces anatomical asymmetry. This, in turn, leads to helical coiling of their shells, almost invariably in a right-handed spiral. The shape of the resulting spiral can assume a staggering variety of forms, many of which are adaptations to particular environments. It is not uncommon for similar shell forms to be exhibited by distantly related snails, as a result of convergent evolutionary adaptations to particular habitats. As in the cephalopods, the shell has become reduced, internal, or lost within several lineages of gastropods.

IDENTIFYING SHELLS

Identifying a shell may seem a daunting task considering there are roughly 100,000 species of mollusks living today. It is best seen as a process of elimination in which you gradually or rapidly narrow the range of possibilities. Simply knowing that you are dealing with a seashell, for example, immediately rules out all the species of mollusks that do not have a shell, as well as all those that do not live in the sea.

The first and most basic stage in the process of identification is to determine the class to which the shell belongs. This is done by counting the number of sections that comprise the shell.

If the shell is composed of eight sections, or valves, it is a chiton, of which there are about 1,000 living species. If the shell is composed of two valves, it is a bivalve (about 20,000 species). If the shell consists of a single section (not counting an operculum), then it could be a scaphopod (about 900 species), a cephalopod (six species with an external shell), or a gastropod (more than 50,000 species).

Scaphopods have a long, tapering, tubular shell open at both ends. Cephalopods have shells that are large, planispiral (coiled in a single plane), and subdivided into chambers connected by a siphuncle. Any single-valved shell that has not previously been excluded is likely to be one of the marine snails (gastropods).

Once the shell has been identified to a class, it needs to be sorted into one of several smaller groups within the class. The identification process continues until the choices are limited to a few species within a single genus, and finally to one of the species within the genus. This is done by comparing the shell directly against known specimens or images until a final identification is achieved.

THE
SHELLS

WEST INDIAN CHITON

LINNAEUS, 1758

SHELL SIZE RANGE
⅜ to 4 in
(10 to 100 mm)

FAMILY ~ Chitonidae

DISTRIBUTION ~ Florida to Venezuela and West Indies

ABUNDANCE ~ Common

DEPTH ~ Intertidal to 13 ft (4 m)

HABITAT ~ Rocky shores

FEEDING HABIT ~ Nocturnal grazer, feeds on algae

Chiton tuberculatus is one of the largest chitons occurring in the Caribbean. It has a handsome shell with a girdle covered by scales that have alternating color bands in white and greenish black. Like most chitons, it is active at night, and feeds by grazing algae on rocks. It has a "homing" behavior, and after short feeding excursions it returns to its original resting place. It may live as long as 12 years. *Chiton tuberculatus* and other chitons occur in high densities locally, and may contribute significantly to the bioerosion of limestone. Chitonids have comblike teeth on the margin of the valves. There are about 100 species in the family Chitonidae worldwide.

The shell of the West Indian Chiton is medium in size and ovate, with the girdle covered by scales. The dorsal surface sculpture consists of about 8 to 9 strong, wavy longitudinal ribs on the triangular areas of each valve, a smooth central strip, and beaded nodules at the terminal valves. The girdle has white and greenish black alternating bands, and the dorsal surface of the valves ranges from grayish to brownish green. The underside of cleaned valves is greenish or bluish white.

DISTRIBUTION

CRYPTOCHITON STELLERI

GUMBOOT CHITON

(MIDDENDORF, 1846)

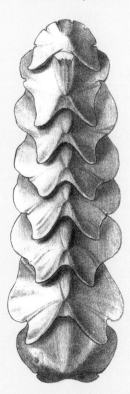

SHELL SIZE RANGE
4 to 16 in
(100 to 400 mm)

FAMILY ~ Acanthochitonidae

DISTRIBUTION ~ Hokkaido, Japan, to Aleutian Islands; Alaska to
southern California

ABUNDANCE ~ Locally common

DEPTH ~ Intertidal to 65 ft (20 m)

HABITAT ~ Rocky shores

FEEDING HABIT ~ Nocturnal grazer, feeds on red algae

Cryptochiton stelleri is the world's largest chiton, reaching 16 in (400 mm) in length and weighting up to 2 lbs (800 g), although it typically grows to about 6 in (150 mm). It is the only chiton that has all eight plates completely covered by the thick, leathery mantle typical of the group. Its broad foot is yellow or orange. *Cryptochiton stelleri* is a traditional source of food for native peoples, despite its tough meat. It is slow-growing, typically taking some 20 years to reach about 6 in (150 mm) in length; it can live more than 25 years. Because of its slow reproduction and overharvesting, there are concerns about its conservation.

The shell of the Gumboot Chiton is large and thick, with plates that are only loosely interconnected. The shell plates are much smaller than the very large body, and they are completely enclosed within the leathery mantle. The 8 plates, when cleaned and articulated, resemble the vertebrae of mammals. When disarticulated most of the plates have a butterfly shape, and are known as "butterfly" shells that often wash up ashore. The shell plates may be white or robin-egg blue in color.

DISTRIBUTION

ATLANTIC TURKEY WING

SWAINSON, 1833

SHELL SIZE RANGE
2 to 4 in
(50 to 100 mm)

FAMILY ~ Arcidae

DISTRIBUTION ~ North Carolina to Brazil

ABUNDANCE ~ Common

DEPTH ~ Intertidal to 460 ft (140 m)

HABITAT ~ Attached to rocks and coral heads

FEEDING HABIT ~ Filter feeder

BYSSUS ~ Present

Arca zebra is a common arcid found in the intertidal zone or shallow waters attached by a byssus to the underside of rocks and coral heads. Its distinctive pattern of purple-brown, zigzag stripes on a white shell resembles the wings of a turkey, hence the popular name. Young turkey wings are usually brightly colored, but coloration fades with increased size. Like other arcids, there are small ocelli on the mantle that are light-sensitive and the animal responds to changes in light intensity and shadows. *Arca zebra* is an important food resource in Venezuela.

The shell of the Atlantic Turkey Wing is medium in size, elongated, and nearly rectangular in outline. It has a long, straight hinge, which can have more than 100 denticles, and prominent umbones; a narrow byssal gape is opposite from the hinge. Its sculpture is dominated by the 24 to 30 irregular radial ribs, crossed by growth ridges. The shell length is about twice the height. The shell is white with purple-brown irregular stripes; the shell has a white center inside and reddish brown margins.

DISTRIBUTION

PERNA VIRIDIS

GREEN MUSSEL

(LINNAEUS, 1758)

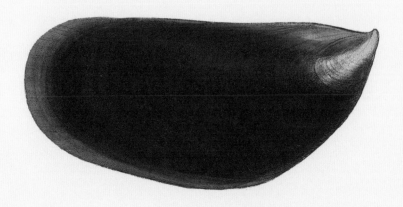

SHELL SIZE RANGE
2¾ to 8 in
(70 to 200 mm)

FAMILY ~ Mytilidae

DISTRIBUTION ~ Indian Ocean to Southwest Pacific

ABUNDANCE ~ Locally abundant

DEPTH ~ Intertidal to 65 ft (20 m)

HABITAT ~ Byssally attached to rocks

FEEDING HABIT ~ Filter feeder

BYSSUS ~ Present

Perna viridis is an edible mussel originally from the coasts of India and widely distributed in the Indo-Pacific Ocean. Because it grows rapidly and has a wide environmental tolerance, it is a successful colonizer and an invasive species. It has been introduced to many places, including Florida, where it is believed to have arrived as larvae in the ballast water of commercial ships. In the West Indies, it is spreading by "island-hopping." It has a potential for cultivation for food, as well as to be used as an indicator species to test for pollution. *Perna viridis* can grow to 8 in (200 mm), although most specimens are less than half of that size.

The shell of the Green Mussel is medium-large, moderately thin but solid, inflated, and triangular in outline. Its umbones are pointed and terminal, located anteriorly. The hinge plates narrow, with 1 small tooth in the right valve and 2 in the left. The sculpture consists of fine growth lines and faint radial striae. Young shells are green with bluish margins; adults grow brown patches. The interior is iridescent pale bluish green.

DISTRIBUTION

PINCTADA MARGARITIFERA

PEARL OYSTER

(LINNAEUS, 1758)

SHELL SIZE RANGE
3 to 12 in
(75 to 300 mm)

FAMILY ~ Pteriidae

DISTRIBUTION ~ Red Sea to Indo-Pacific

ABUNDANCE ~ Common

DEPTH ~ Shallow subtidal to 215 ft (65 m)

HABITAT ~ Byssally attached to rocks

FEEDING HABIT ~ Filter-feeder

BYSSUS ~ Present

Pinctada margaritifera is one of the main sources of natural or cultivated pearls. It is widely distributed in the Red Sea and throughout the Indo-Pacific; it has been introduced to Florida. Potentially any mollusk can produce pearls, and many species do, but those produced by *P. margaritifera* are of the highest quality. Its name means "pearl bearer." The color of its nacre and pearls varies widely, from white to gray to shades of yellow, rose, or green; there are also the famous Tahitian black pearls, which are usually dark gray or brown. There are about 70 living species in the family Pteriidae in warm waters worldwide.

The shell of the Pearl Oyster is large, thick, and subcircular in outline. The posterior and anterior ears are poorly developed. Its sculpture consists of flat concentric scales that project beyond the shell margin. The hinge is straight and toothless. The outside color is dark brown or green with radial white rays; inside, the shell has a thick and shiny nacreous layer, which varies widely in color from silver to green or dark gray; the shell margin lacks nacre and is dark.

DISTRIBUTION

WHITE HAMMER OYSTER

LAMARCK, 1819

SHELL SIZE RANGE
6 to 12 in
(150 to 300 mm)

FAMILY ~ Malleidae

DISTRIBUTION ~ Indo-Pacific

ABUNDANCE ~ Common

DEPTH ~ 3 to 100 ft (1 to 30 m)

HABITAT ~ Muddy sand bottoms

FEEDING HABIT ~ Filter feeder

BYSSUS ~ Absent in adults

Malleus albus has a very distinctive shell, shaped like a pick ax or a hammer. Like other malleids, its shell is irregularly shaped, in part because of break and repair; the mantle can mend broken parts of the shell rather quickly. Young shells are short and become very long as they grow. *Malleus albus* lives freely on the surface of fine muddy sand bottoms, and loses the byssus during growth. The long projections of the hinge help stabilize the shell on the soft sediment, and prevent the shell from being turned over. It is found in large colonies in some areas.

The shell of the White Hammer Oyster is large, thick, and irregularly shaped like a hammer. Its hinge is long and straight, and both the anterior and posterior extremities of the hinge become elongated. The "handle" of the hammer is the ventral margin, which becomes undulating and extremely developed in adults. The umbones are located at about the mid-point of the hinge, near the dorsal margin. The shell color is dirty white outside, and gray or bluish nacreous inside near the ligament.

DISTRIBUTION

PINNA RUGOSA

RUGOSE PEN SHELL

SOWERBY I, 1835

SHELL SIZE RANGE
4 to 23¼ in
(100 to 590 mm)

FAMILY ~ Pinnidae

DISTRIBUTION ~ Baja California to Ecuador and the
Galápagos Islands

ABUNDANCE ~ Common

DEPTH ~ Intertidal to shallow subtidal

HABITAT ~ Muddy bottoms in mangroves

FEEDING HABIT ~ Filter feeder

BYSSUS ~ Present

Pinna rugosa is a large pen shell common in muddy bottoms in quiet bays and mangroves. It has been used traditionally by the Seri Indians from Sonora, western Mexico, as a sustainable food resource. Pinnid shells are poorly calcified and have a high content of organic matter, making them flexible to the point that the anterior gape can be closed by muscular contraction. Dried shells become brittle and can crack. Pinnids are called pen shells because of the vague resemblance to old-style writing quills. Another name, razor clams, comes from the sharp posterior edge that projects outside of the sediment.

The shell of the Rugose Pen Shell is large, flexible, fragile, translucent, and triangular elongated. It has about 8 rows of large tubular spines, which are largest near the posterior end; in old specimens the spines may be worn down. The anterior end is slender, pointed, and smooth. The posterior end is broad, about half of the shell length in width. The shell color is light brown and its interior is partly nacreous.

DISTRIBUTION

NODIPECTEN NODOSUS

LION'S PAW

(LINNAEUS, 1758)

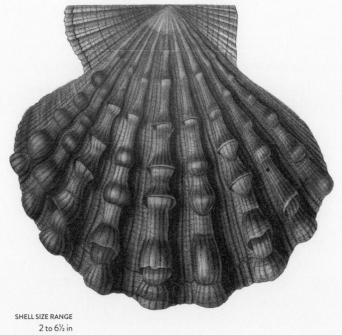

SHELL SIZE RANGE
2 to 6½ in
(50 to 170 mm)

FAMILY ~ Pectinidae

DISTRIBUTION ~ Caribbean to Brazil

ABUNDANCE ~ Common

DEPTH ~ Intertidal to 500 ft (150 m)

HABITAT ~ Attached by byssus to rocks

FEEDING HABIT ~ Filter feeder

BYSSUS ~ Present

Nodipecten nodosus is one of the largest scallops in the western Atlantic. It has a very distinctive shell, with several coarse radial ribs bearing hollow knobs; it is usually colored reddish brown but is sometimes bright red, yellow, or orange. Its cultivation for food is still under development in some parts of South America. In culture, *N. nodosus* grows faster at a shallow depth, but has a higher survival rate at greater depths. This species lives attached to rocks and other hard substrates, including shipwrecks and artificial reefs.

The shell of the Lion's Paw is large, thick, heavy, and moderately convex, with a broad fan shape. Each valve has about 7 to 10 large, coarse ribs, which bear hollow knobs arranged in concentric rows; the whole shell is covered by strong radial riblets, and crossed by concentric ridges. The posterior ear is about half the length of the anterior. Inside the valves, the radial ribs show as deep channels. The shell color varies from reddish brown to bright orange or yellow, and the interior is purplish brown.

DISTRIBUTION

AMERICAN THORNY OYSTER

HERMANN, 1781

SHELL SIZE RANGE
3 to 6 in
(76 to 150 mm)

FAMILY ~ Spondylidae

DISTRIBUTION ~ North Carolina to Brazil

ABUNDANCE ~ Common

DEPTH ~ Intertidal to 460 ft (140 m)

HABITAT ~ Cemented to hard substrates

FEEDING HABIT ~ Filter feeder

BYSSUS ~ Absent

Spondylus americanus is a large, spinose, and colorful spondylid that is particularly common on the thousands of offshore oil rigs in the Gulf of Mexico. The world record size for this species is 9½ in (241.5 mm) in length, probably including the spines. It grows cemented by the right valve to rocks, corals, and other hard substrates. The shell is heavily encrusted with sponges, corals, and other marine life, making it well camouflaged.

The shell of the American Thorny Oyster is large, heavy, solid, and oval to circular. Its valves have different sizes and shapes, and are decorated with radial ribs and erect spines up to 3 in (75 mm) long. The right valve, permanently cemented to the substrate, is larger than the upper (left) valve. The hinge structure has strong interlocking teeth that form a ball-and-socket type joint. The shell color is variable, from white to yellow and red, and the interior is white with reddish purple near the margins.

DISTRIBUTION

CARIBBEAN PIDDOCK CLAM

SOWERBY I, 1823

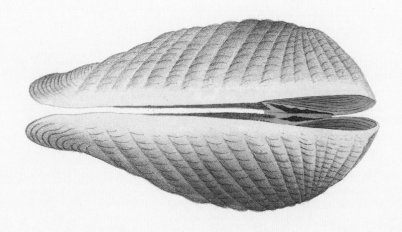

SHELL SIZE RANGE
2 to 5 in
(75 to 130 mm)

FAMILY ~ Pholadomyidae

DISTRIBUTION ~ Caribbean to Colombia

ABUNDANCE ~ Extremely rare

DEPTH ~ Shallow intertidal to 80 ft (25 m)

HABITAT ~ Sandy bottoms

FEEDING HABIT ~ Deposit feeder

BYSSUS ~ Absent

Pholadomya candida is among the rarest of bivalves, and is considered to be a living fossil. Several specimens had been collected in the early nineteenth century. It was believed to be extinct until additional shells were collected along the Caribbean coast of Colombia, including a live specimen that was found buried deep in coarse sand in shallow water. *Pholadomya candida* has a pair of large, fused siphons that extend through the gaping valves. The Pholadomyidae are an ancient group of burrowing bivalves that flourished during the Jurassic and Cretaceous Periods, being represented today by only about ten living species.

The shell of the Caribbean Piddock Clam is very thin, fragile, and posteriorly elongated, with a posterior siphonal gape. The umbones are pronounced, rounded, and situated very close together. The hinge is almost smooth, has a short tubercle and pit, and a short external ligament. The shell has strong radial ribs crossed by concentric growth lines. The central 8 or 9 radial ribs are more pronounced, forming a cancellate pattern of beads. The interior of the shell is pitted and nacreous. The color is white both outside and inside.

DISTRIBUTION

VERPA PENIS

COMMON WATERING POT

(LINNAEUS, 1758)

SHELL SIZE RANGE
3 to 8 in
(75 to 200 mm)

FAMILY ~ Penicillidae

DISTRIBUTION ~ Indo-West Pacific

ABUNDANCE ~ Uncommon

DEPTH ~ 135 to 265 ft (40 to 80 m)

HABITAT ~ Sandy or muddy bottoms

FEEDING HABIT ~ Filter feeder

BYSSUS ~ Absent

Verpa penis is a very distinct and unusual bivalve. Juveniles live freely and have normal shaped shells. When the animal starts to grow, however, it forms a calcareous tube, in which its vestigial shell becomes embedded. The anterior end of the tube is broad and is kept buried in the sediment surface; it has a rounded disk, with many short tubes, and a frilly collar. It is reminiscent of a daisy or the spout of a watering pot. The posterior end of the tube is narrow and open, and is kept just at the surface of the sediment. There are about 15 living species in the family Penicillidae worldwide.

The shell of the Common Watering Pot is very small, oval, and embedded into a large calcareous tube. Its valves have different sizes, and lack a hinge plate. The anterior end of the calcareous tube has a perforated disk with many short tubes, and a pleated collar. The tube, which has a sculpture of fine concentric lines, tapers to a narrow and posterior open end, through which the siphons reach the surface. The valves and tube are chalky white.

DISTRIBUTION

TRUE HEART COCKLE

(LINNAEUS, 1758)

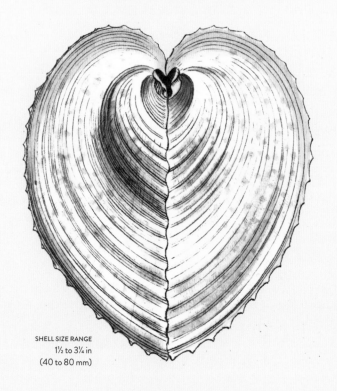

SHELL SIZE RANGE
1½ to 3¼ in
(40 to 80 mm)

FAMILY ~ Cardiidae

DISTRIBUTION ~ Red Sea to Indo-West Pacific

ABUNDANCE ~ Abundant

DEPTH ~ Intertidal to 65 ft (20 m)

HABITAT ~ Sandy bottoms among reefs

FEEDING HABIT ~ Grows symbiotic algae

BYSSUS ~ Present

Corculum cardissa has a curiously distorted shell: it is strongly compressed anteroposteriorly but expanded laterally, forming a sharp keel that is heart-shaped in outline. One side is concave and the other convex. It is a common species that lives near coral reefs, and can form dense colonies. It rests horizontally with its flatter side down on sandy bottoms in shallow water. The shell is thin, with small translucent "windows" that allow light to reach inside the shell. Like the related giant clams, *C. cardissa* grows symbiotic algae within its mantle and gills, which provide nutrients to the clam. Its shell is collected and used for shellcraft.

The shell of the True Heart Cockle is medium in size, thin, and anteroposteriorly compressed but greatly expanded laterally, with a heart-shape outline. Its umbones are overlapping, and curve sharply. The valves are unequal in size and shape; the shape is variable. The sculpture consists of radial ribs; there is a strong keel in the periphery of the shell, which bears spiny projections. The shell color varies from white to yellow and pink, with a similar color inside.

DISTRIBUTION

SPINY VENUS

(LESSON, 1831)

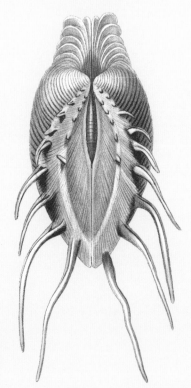

SHELL SIZE RANGE
1¼ to 3¼ in
(30 to 80 mm)

FAMILY ~ Veneridae

DISTRIBUTION ~ Western Mexico to Peru

ABUNDANCE ~ Common

DEPTH ~ Intertidal to 80 ft (25 m)

HABITAT ~ Infaunal in sandy bottoms

FEEDING HABIT ~ Filter feeder

BYSSUS ~ Absent

Hysteroconcha lupanaria is one of the most spectacular clams, with long, erect spines, and a colorful shell. It is one of only a few species in the genus *Hysteroconcha* in the large family Veneridae to have spines on the shell, and *H. lupanaria* has the longest ones; most other species in the genus lack spines. The clam lives buried in sand in shallow water, with the spines pointing upward, surrounding its siphons. The spines may protect the siphons from predators. *Pitar lupanaria* is commonly found washed ashore on sandy beaches, especially after a storm.

The shell of the Spiny Venus is medium in size, solid, moderately thick and inflated, and ovately triangular in outline. Its valves have wide, erect, concentric ribs that are stronger anteriorly, and end in 2 radial rows of long and short, pointed, and open spines posteriorly. The umbones are prominent and pointed anteriorly. The shell is creamy white to pale pink, tinged with violet and with violet blotches at the base of the spines; the interior is white.

DISTRIBUTION

WEDDING CAKE VENUS

(PERRY, 1811)

SHELL SIZE RANGE
1½ to 3 in
(40 to 75 mm)

FAMILY ~ Veneridae

DISTRIBUTION ~ New South Wales to South Australia

ABUNDANCE ~ Common

DEPTH ~ Shallow subtidal to 165 ft (50 m)

HABITAT ~ Sandy mud banks

FEEDING HABIT ~ Filter feeder

BYSSUS ~ Absent in adults

Bassina disjecta has a beautiful and distinctive shell, rounded and triangular with frilly lamellose concentric ribs. It is usually found in shallow subtidal depths, in tropical and temperate waters, in sandy mud banks. It is a shallow burrower, and lies buried with the posterior margin of the shell close to the surface. The animal has two siphons, one inhalant and one exhalant, which allow it to remain buried in the sediment and circulate water through ciliary pumping. The lamellose ribs help stabilize the shell in the fine sediment.

The shell of the Wedding Cake Venus is medium in size, thin but solid, compressed, and rounded triangular to elongately ovate in outline. Its most prominent feature is the presence of about 6 to 8 broadly spaced, lamellose concentric ribs that are frilly and turned upward at the edges. The umbones are small and anteriorly facing. The valves are identical in size and shape. The shell color is white, sometimes with pink on the lower side of the lamellae, and it has a white interior.

DISTRIBUTION

ASAPHIS VIOLASCENS

PACIFIC ASAPHIS

(FORSSKÅL IN NIEBUHR, 1775)

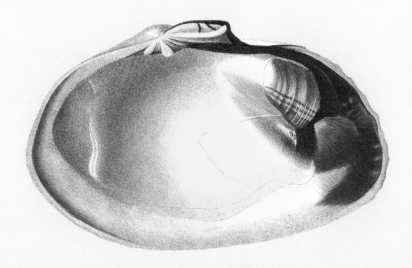

SHELL SIZE RANGE
1¾ to 3 in
(45 to 75 mm)

FAMILY ~ Psammobiidae

DISTRIBUTION ~ Red Sea to Indo-Pacific

ABUNDANCE ~ Common

DEPTH ~ Intertidal to 65 ft (20 m)

HABITAT ~ Coarse and fine sandy bottoms

FEEDING HABIT ~ Suspension feeder

BYSSUS ~ Absent

Asaphis violascens is a deep-burrowing clam that can burrow to a depth of about 8 in (20 cm). It lives in coarse sandy or gravelly bottoms. It is common in shallow tropical waters, ranging from the Red Sea, throughout the Indian Ocean, and to the central Pacific. It is collected for food, marketed locally, and its shell is used in shellcraft. In China, it can reach densities of up to 50 clams per sq yd (60 per m²). Psammobiids are infaunal bivalves, often found in sediment with high organic content. Most species are believed to be deposit feeders, although some are filter feeders.

The shell of the Pacific Asaphis is medium in size, moderately inflated, thick, and elongately ovate in outline. Its umbones are rounded and situated anteriorly, and the hinge line has 2 cardinal teeth in each valve. The anterior margin is rounded and the posterior is subtruncate. The sculpture consists of numerous strong radial ribs and weaker concentric growth lines. The shell color is white, tinged with purple or orange rays, and the interior is yellow and purple.

DISTRIBUTION

GIANT RAZOR SHELL

(LINNAEUS, 1758)

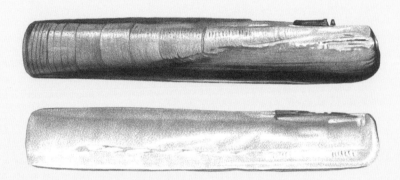

SHELL SIZE RANGE
6 to 9 in
(150 to 230 mm)

FAMILY ~ Pharidae

DISTRIBUTION ~ Norway to Iberian Peninsula; Mediterranean

ABUNDANCE ~ Common

DEPTH ~ Intertidal to 230 ft (70 m)

HABITAT ~ Fine sand and mud

FEEDING HABIT ~ Filter feeder

BYSSUS ~ Absent

Ensis siliqua is the largest species in the family Pharidae, with some shells reaching 9 in (230 mm) in length and 1 in (25 mm) in width. The shell is very elongate and narrow, and resembles the old-style razors, hence the popular name of razor or jackknife clams. *Ensis siliqua* lives in deep vertical burrows in fine sandy bottoms, in intertidal flats and offshore. It can bury itself rapidly to a depth of up to 20 ft (6 m). The shells in the genus *Ensis* are similar, and muscle scars are useful in identification. *Ensis siliqua* was formerly abundant around Belgium, but now *E. directus* is the dominant species.

The shell of the Giant Razor Shell is large, thin, fragile, inflated, and elongate-rectangular in outline. Its umbones are inconspicuous, located close to the anterior margin; the hinge is narrow, with small teeth. The sculpture consists of smooth concentric lines, and a diagonal line from the umbones to the posterior ventral edge. The valves are identical in size and shape, and gape at both ends. The shell color is whitish with violet-brown stains, with a yellow-brown periostracum. The shell interior is white and has purple tints.

DISTRIBUTION

NAVAL SHIPWORM

LINNAEUS, 1758

SHELL SIZE RANGE
¹⁄₁₆ to ½ in
(2 to 12 mm)

FAMILY ~ Teredinidae

DISTRIBUTION ~ Cosmopolitan

ABUNDANCE ~ Common

DEPTH ~ Intertidal to 26 ft (8 m)

HABITAT ~ Bores into wood primarily

FEEDING HABIT ~ Primarily xylophagous; also filter feeder

BYSSUS ~ Absent

Teredo navalis is perhaps the bivalve that has caused the most economic damage through the destruction of wooden boats, piers, and other wooden structures into which it bores. Shipworms have a reduced shell, a long, wormlike body, and calcareous structures, called pallets, that plug the entrance of the burrow. The pallets are more important in species identification than the shells, which vary little between species. The animal bores into wood by mechanical abrasion, using its modified shell. There are about 70 living species in the family Teredinidae, most in tropical shallow waters worldwide.

The shell of the Naval Shipworm is vestigial, minute, thin, inflated, trilobed, and helmetlike in outline. Its valves are identical in size and shape, and gape widely both anteroventrally and posteriorly; there is a deep, right-angled notch. The anterior surface of the valves is finely sculpted with rows of minute teeth, which are used to rasp the wood. There is a long and narrow rib near the umbo. The shell color is white, as are the simple and paddlelike pallets.

DISTRIBUTION

ELEPHANT TUSK

LINNAEUS, 1758

SHELL SIZE RANGE
2 to 4 in
(50 to 100 mm)

FAMILY ~ Dentaliidae

DISTRIBUTION ~ Red Sea to Australia

ABUNDANCE ~ Uncommon

DEPTH ~ Intertidal to 133 ft (40 m)

HABITAT ~ Sandy bottoms

FEEDING HABIT ~ Micro-omnivore, primarily foraminiferans

Dentalium elephantinum is a large, thick scaphopod that is easily recognized by its dark green color anteriorly, which fades to white posteriorly. It lives buried in sandy bottoms with the posterior (narrow) end sticking out of the surface. *Dentalium elephantinum* is the type species of the genus. Empty shells of scaphopods are often inhabited by hermit crabs and sipunculan worms. Some hermit crabs have become specialized to live exclusively in scaphopod shells, with one cheliped serving as an operculum to plug the shell. There are more than 200 living species in the family Dentaliidae worldwide. The family's fossil record extends to the mid-Triassic Period.

The shell of the Elephant Tusk is large, thick, solid, heavy, colorful, and slightly curved. Its anterior end is rounded, wide, and about three times as wide as the posterior end. There is a notch in the posterior end. The sculpture consists of about 10 strong, rounded longitudinal ribs that run the entire length of the shell, and fine growth lines. The shell color is dark green near the anterior end, fading to white toward the posterior opening.

DISTRIBUTION

SCUTELLASTRA LONGICOSTA

LONG-RIBBED LIMPET

(LAMARCK, 1819)

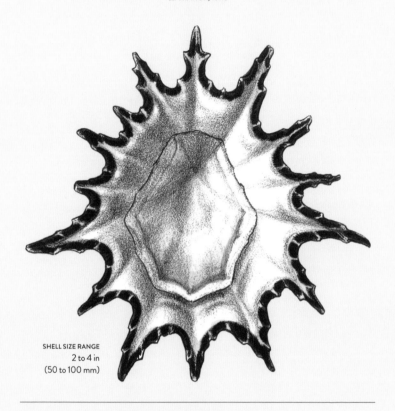

SHELL SIZE RANGE
2 to 4 in
(50 to 100 mm)

FAMILY ~ Patellidae

DISTRIBUTION ~ South Africa to Mozambique

ABUNDANCE ~ Common

DEPTH ~ Intertidal

HABITAT ~ Rocky shores

FEEDING HABIT ~ Grazer, feeds on crustose brown algae

OPERCULUM ~ Absent

Despite being variable in shell shape, *Scutellastra longicosta* is easily recognizable in having the longest radiating ribs among the several star-shaped limpets. The radial ridges add strength to the shell, and also help disperse the force of breaking waves through the shell. *Scutellastra longicosta* is a common limpet on intertidal rocks, occurring mostly in South Africa but also found in Mozambique. Its ecology is well known, and studies have shown *S. longicosta* to be a territorial limpet that has a mutually beneficial relationship with the crustose brown alga *Ralfsia verrucosa*, maintaining an algal garden around its home scar, an indentation in the rock to which it returns.

The shell of the Long-ribbed Limpet is large, thick, solid, and star-shaped. There are 10 major ridges that project radially as sharp points of a star, as well as a few smaller intermediate ridges. The shell color is dark or light brown, and the shell is often encrusted with algae. The interior is porcellaneous white, with the central muscle scar brownish.

DISTRIBUTION

CELLANA MAZATLANDICA

BONIN ISLAND LIMPET

(SOWERBY I, 1839)

SHELL SIZE RANGE
1¾ to 3½ in
(45 to 90 mm)

FAMILY ~ Nacellidae

DISTRIBUTION ~ Endemic to Bonin Islands, Japan

ABUNDANCE ~ Abundant

DEPTH ~ Intertidal

HABITAT ~ Rocky shores

FEEDING HABIT ~ Grazer, feeds on algae

OPERCULUM ~ Absent

Cellana mazatlandica is a limpet with a very limited distribution; it is restricted to the Bonin Islands (Ogasawara Islands), an archipelago of 30 islands located about 620 miles (1,000 km) directly south of Tokyo, and halfway between Tokyo and Guam. It is locally abundant, living on intertidal rocks. Field studies suggest its life span is about three to four years. In 1966, an attempted introduction into Guam to develop its fishery failed, but transplant experiments within the Bonin Islands have been successful. The species name was given in error for Mazatlán, in western Mexico. A better name, *boninensis*, was proposed by Pilsbry in 1891, but *mazatlandica* has priority.

The shell of the Bonin Island Limpet is medium in size, relatively thin, conic, and ovate. The apex is acute and located slightly off-center, closer to the anterior end. The sculpture consists of about 40 strong and scaly radial ridges that alternate with intermediary ones, and concentric growth lines that coincide with concentric bands of varying colors. The margin of the shell is scalloped. The shell color is usually dull light brown to orange, and the interior silvery with a light brown margin and a brown muscle scar.

DISTRIBUTION

RUMPHIUS' SLIT SHELL

(SCHEPMAN, 1879)

SHELL SIZE RANGE
6 to 10 in
(150 to 250 mm)

FAMILY ~ Pleurotomariidae

DISTRIBUTION ~ Southern Japan to Philippines

ABUNDANCE ~ Rare

DEPTH ~ Deep water, to 1,000 ft (300 m)

HABITAT ~ Rocky bottoms

FEEDING HABIT ~ Carnivore, feeds on sponges

OPERCULUM ~ Corneous, multispiral, and large

Entemnotrochus rumphii is the largest species of slit shell. Like other slit shells, it lives in deep water and feeds on sponges. Slit shells all have corneous opercula; some species, such as *Mikadotrochus hirasei*, have a small operculum, but all species of *Entemnotrochus* have a large operculum that plugs the aperture. The ancestors of slit shells are among the oldest gastropods, having appeared some 500 million years ago. Pleurotomariids were once more diverse, but only about 36 recent species are currently known. Because of their deepwater habitat, most species are considered rare, but recent data suggests that some are fairly common in their habitat.

The shell of the Rumphius' Slit Shell is large and heavy yet fragile. It has a tall spire and a narrow and very long slit. The suture is well impressed. The spire whorls are slightly convex and the narrow selenizone divides the whorls in about half. Its sculpture comprises fine spiral lines and oblique axial lines that coincide with reddish streaks against a creamy white background. The aperture is large and nacreous, and the umbilicus is wide and deep.

DISTRIBUTION

HALIOTIS SCALARIS

STAIRCASE ABALONE

(LEACH, 1814)

SHELL SIZE RANGE
2½ to 4 in
(60 to 100 mm)

FAMILY ~ Haliotidae

DISTRIBUTION ~ Endemic from Western to South Australia

ABUNDANCE ~ Common

DEPTH ~ Intertidal to shallow subtidal

HABITAT ~ Rocky bottoms

FEEDING HABIT ~ Herbivore, grazes on algae

OPERCULUM ~ Absent

Haliotis scalaris is one of the most distinctive and beautiful of the Australian abalones. Its outer sculpture is complex and the main feature is a central spiral fold, with radial lamellae running from the central fold to the previous whorl. It is endemic to Australia, ranging from Western to South Australia. It is found from the intertidal to subtidal zones, under rocks; it is common but never abundant. Like other abalones, it has a depressed and loosely coiled shell.

The shell of the Staircase Abalone is medium in size, thin, and oval in outline. Its spire is moderately elevated, located closer to the posterior margin, and has about 3 whorls. The tremata are elevated, and the last 4 to 6 holes are open. The sculpture is dominated by a strong, central spiral fold and oblique radial lamellae that run from this fold to the previous whorl. There are also other weaker radial and spiral elements; the main ones show in the interior, which is smooth and nacreous. The shell color is orange-red, with curved, radiating cream rays.

DISTRIBUTION

HALIOTIS ASININA

DONKEY'S EAR ABALONE

LINNAEUS, 1758

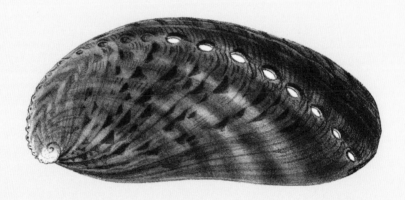

SHELL SIZE RANGE
2½ to 4½ in
(60 to 120 mm)

FAMILY ~ Haliotidae

DISTRIBUTION ~ Indo-West Pacific

ABUNDANCE ~ Abundant

DEPTH ~ Intertidal to 33 ft (10 m)

HABITAT ~ Rocky

FEEDING HABIT ~ Herbivore, grazes on algae

OPERCULUM ~ Absent

Haliotis asinina is a common species in the tropical Indo-West Pacific. Abalones are herbivores, grazing on algae on rocky substrates. They have a large muscular foot, and can have short bursts of "rapid" movement when necessary to escape predators. The shell has a row of holes, called tremata, near the periphery of the whorl, which are used to exhale water. As the shell grows, the oldest holes are filled, and new ones are formed near the edge of the shell. Where large species occur, abalones are used for food. Their nacreous shells are used in jewelry.

The shell of the Donkey's Ear Abalone is thin and elliptical, with the apex near the edge of the shell. It is easily recognized by its elongated shell, which has the highest shell length-to-width ratio in the family. There are 6 to 8 open, ovate holes. The exterior is smooth, with axial growth lines that are crossed by low spiral ridges. The coloration is variable, usually olive green with blotches of brown and cream. The interior is nacreous and white, with a greenish tint.

DISTRIBUTION

MEGATHURA CRENULATA

GREAT KEYHOLE LIMPET

(SOWERBY I, 1825)

SHELL SIZE RANGE
2½ to 5¼ in
(60 to 132 mm)

FAMILY ~ Fissurellidae

DISTRIBUTION ~ California to Baja California

ABUNDANCE ~ Common

DEPTH ~ Intertidal to shallow subtidal

HABITAT ~ Rocky shores

FEEDING HABIT ~ Grazer, feeds on algae and tunicates

OPERCULUM ~ Absent

Megathura crenulata is one of the larger species of keyhole limpet, although not the largest. The genus name comes from the Greek word for "large door," in reference to the shell's large, oval keyhole. It is a common limpet, usually found crawling on shallow subtidal rocks in kelp forests, where it feeds on algae and colonial tunicates. *Megathura crenulata* is unique among limpets because its black or gray mantle covers most or all of the shell, showing only the "keyhole." Its hemolymph ("blood") has promising biomedical applications, therefore several companies are currently investing in its aquaculture.

The shell of the Great Keyhole Limpet is large, low, thick, and elliptical in profile. The dorsal foramen, the keyhole, is large, oval, and subcentral. Its sculpture comprises fine, regularly spaced radial ribs and concentric lines. The margin of the shell is irregular and bears small denticles. The dorsal color ranges from reddish brown to gray, and the interior is porcelaneous white. The keyhole margin is white.

DISTRIBUTION

ANGARIA MELANACANTHA

IMPERIAL DELPHINULA

(REEVE, 1842)

SHELL SIZE RANGE
1⅜ to 2¾ in
(35 to 70 mm)

FAMILY ~ Turbinidae

DISTRIBUTION ~ West Pacific

ABUNDANCE ~ Locally abundant

DEPTH ~ Deep water

HABITAT ~ Coral reefs and hard bottoms

FEEDING HABIT ~ Herbivore, grazes on algae

OPERCULUM ~ Corneous, concentric, circular

Angaria melanacantha is a common to abundant species living in deeper water near coral reefs. This and many other gastropods are usually collected using tangle nets in the Philippines. Its shell has many spines that vary in development and can grow quite long in some specimens, much longer in calmer waters than in areas with stronger currents. The shells are usually encrusted with algae, corals, and other organisms, and it takes careful work to clean them in order to reveal the perfect shells seen in collections. The operculum is rounded, multispiral, and corneous, unlike those of most turbinids, which have a calcareous operculum.

The shell of the Imperial Delphinula is thick, depressed, very spinose, and has a short spire. The large body whorl dominates the shell. The shoulder has long spines that curve upward and inward, while the rest of the shell is covered with several spiral rows of spines. The umbilicus is deep and spinose. The shell color is grayish purple to brown, and the aperture is round, nacreous, and white.

DISTRIBUTION

ROCHIA NILOTICA

COMMERCIAL TOP

(LINNAEUS, 1767)

SHELL SIZE RANGE
2 to 6 in
(50 to 150 mm)

FAMILY ~ Trochidae

DISTRIBUTION ~ Indo-Pacific

ABUNDANCE ~ Abundant

DEPTH ~ Subtidal to 60 ft (20 m)

HABITAT ~ On or near coral reefs

FEEDING HABIT ~ Herbivore

OPERCULUM ~ Corneous, circular

The common name of *Rochia nilotica* refers to its widespread use as a source of mother-of-pearl for buttons and jewelry. It is the largest of the top shells and has the added attraction to commercial fishermen of being edible; the large foot of the animal is boiled and smoked. It is currently fished in modest quantities, mostly for the decorative trade. It is a striking shell, popular with both collectors and interior designers.

The shell of the Commercial Top is equilateral in profile and smooth apart from the protoconch, which has hollow axial tubercles on the younger whorls. Mature specimens have a broadly bulging final whorl. The shell is white, with a pattern of broad axial bands of dark red-brown. The bottom is concave, and it lacks an umbilicus. The very open downward sloping aperture has a thin outer lip and a labial ridge on the columella.

DISTRIBUTION

GIANT KNOBBED CERITH

BRUGUIÈRE, 1792

SHELL SIZE RANGE
2½ to 6 in
(60 to 150 mm)

FAMILY ~ Cerithiidae

DISTRIBUTION ~ Indo-West Pacific

ABUNDANCE ~ Abundant

DEPTH ~ Intertidal to shallow subtidal

HABITAT ~ Sand, rubble, and reef flats

FEEDING HABIT ~ Grazer, feeds on microalgal detritus

OPERCULUM ~ Corneous, ovate, with few whorls

Cerithium nodulosum is the largest species in the genus *Cerithium* and one of the largest living cerithiids. It is widespread throughout the Indo-West Pacific, abundant in shallow water on sand, rubble, and reef flats, near the outer edge of reefs. While the identification of most ceriths is difficult because many species are variable and may have similar shells, *C. nodulosum* is easily recognized because of its large size and knobbed sculpture. It is collected for food and the shell trade. Females lay egg masses with a thick axial base that is attached to the substrate, and long filaments with eggs that contain an estimated 66,000 eggs.

The shell of the Giant Knobbed Cerith is large for the family, thick, solid, elongate, and heavily sculptured. Its spire is tall, the suture is well marked, and the spire whorls are strongly angulated at the periphery. Each whorl has a single spiral row of strong tubercles and other weaker spiral ribs. The body whorl and aperture are large, and the outer lip thickened and flared and crenulated in adults. The shell color is dirty white with gray-brown blotches. The aperture is white.

DISTRIBUTION

GREAT SCREW SHELL

(LINNAEUS, 1758)

SHELL SIZE RANGE
2½ to 6½ in
(60 to 170 mm)

FAMILY ~ Turritellidae

DISTRIBUTION ~ Indo-West Pacific

ABUNDANCE ~ Abundant

DEPTH ~ Shallow subtidal to 100 ft (30 m)

HABITAT ~ Sandy, muddy bottoms

FEEDING HABIT ~ Suspension feeder

OPERCULUM ~ Corneous, circular

Turritella terebra is variously known as the Great, Common, or Tower Screw Shell or the Screw Turritella. The Great Screw Shell is abundant and the largest member of the screw shell family, all of which are offshore herbivores. Despite its strikingly tall, perfectly formed spire, the species is not particularly popular with collectors, most likely due to its uniform brown coloring, which is devoid of any markings or patterns. Despite being generally abundant, the species is listed as "vulnerable" in Singapore due to land reclamation.

The shell of the Great Screw Shell is notable for its long, very sharp spire, which in adults can be made up of around 30 whorls. Separated by deep sutures, each whorl has 6 clearly defined spiral ridges, with smaller ridges in between. The almost perfectly round aperture is bounded by a thin columella and sharp outer lip. The color ranges from pale to dark brown.

DISTRIBUTION

TENAGODUS SQUAMATUS

SLIT WORM SNAIL

(BLAINVILLE, 1827)

SHELL SIZE RANGE
1½ to 6 in
(40 to 150 mm)

FAMILY ~ Siliquariidae

DISTRIBUTION ~ North Carolina to northern Brazil

ABUNDANCE ~ Common

DEPTH ~ 80 to 2,400 ft (25 to 730 m)

HABITAT ~ Embedded in sponges

FEEDING HABIT ~ Filter feeder

OPERCULUM ~ Corneous, conical

Tenagodus squamatus has an irregularly coiled shell in which the whorls become completely detached. It lives embedded in sponges, and, like the sponge, it is a filter-feeder. Because the sponge supports the weight of the shell, some functional constraints on shell morphology are relaxed, and the result is a very irregular shell. However, the snail needs to keep up with the growth of the sponge to keep the shell aperture open to the outside. There are about 20 living species in the family Siliquariidae worldwide. Some, but not all, species have a continuous slit on the shell, like *T. squamatus*.

The shell of the Slit Worm Snail is medium-sized, thin, fragile, and irregularly coiled. Its spire starts as a conical shell, but is often missing. The whorls are loosely coiled or not coiled at all, with a long, continuous slit that can be smooth or constricted in places. The surface can be smooth or have spiral ridges with scales. The aperture is rounded and the outer lip simple and thin. The slit opens more widely anteriorly. The shell color is off-white, stained a pale orange-brown along the slit.

DISTRIBUTION

TELESCOPE SNAIL

(LINNAEUS, 1758)

SHELL SIZE RANGE
2 to 4½ in
(48 to 120 mm)

FAMILY ~ Potamididae

DISTRIBUTION ~ Indo-West Pacific

ABUNDANCE ~ Abundant

DEPTH ~ Intertidal

HABITAT ~ Mangroves and mud flats

FEEDING HABIT ~ Detritivore, feeds on organic detritus

OPERCULUM ~ Corneous, multispiral, circular

Telescopium telescopium is an abundant snail found in the high intertidal zone in mangroves and intertidal mud flats, where it feeds on organic detritus. It may be seen in aggregations of many thousands at times. Because *T. telescopium* is an amphibious snail, it can stay out of the water for long periods, but during low tides, it clusters together with other snails and becomes inactive. Like some other potamidids, it has a third eye on the mantle, which is capable of sensing light, in addition to the pair of eyes on the cephalic tentacles. It is used as food in Southeast Asia.

The shell of the Telescope Snail is medium-sized, thick, heavy, and conical with a tall spire. Its spire has many whorls, and the suture is weak. The sculpture of the spire consists of 4 strong, flat spiral cords of unequal size alternating with deep spiral grooves. Its base is flat and the body whorl has a rounded periphery. The aperture is relatively small and obliquely quadrangular, and the columella strongly twisted. The shell color is dark brown or black, sometimes with a light brown band, and the aperture is purplish.

DISTRIBUTION

LITTORARIA ZEBRA

ZEBRA PERIWINKLE

(DONOVAN, 1825)

SHELL SIZE RANGE
¾ to 1¼ in
(20 to 30 mm)

FAMILY ~ Littorinidae

DISTRIBUTION ~ Costa Rica to Colombia

ABUNDANCE ~ Moderately common

DEPTH ~ Intertidal

HABITAT ~ Mangroves

FEEDING HABIT ~ Herbivore

OPERCULUM ~ Corneous

Littoraria zebra is considered by collectors as one of the most attractive species in the family, with an unusually colorful shell. Like many periwinkles, it lives on the roots and stems of mangroves. It is endemic to a rather narrow region, the western shores of Central America, which suggests a low tolerance to variations in habitat and temperature.

The shell of the Zebra Periwinkle is a squarish globe with pronounced high shoulders on the body whorl and a moderately low, but deeply sutured, spire. It is pale terra-cotta with oblique brown stripes across very fine spiral cords. The aperture is widely ovate with a thin, extended outer lip within which the pattern shows as a row of brown dots around the rim.

DISTRIBUTION

PAGODA PRICKLY WINKLE

(LINNAEUS, 1758)

SHELL SIZE RANGE
1¼ to 2⅝ in
(30 to 65 mm)

FAMILY ~ Littorinidae

DISTRIBUTION ~ Indo-West Pacific

ABUNDANCE ~ Common

DEPTH ~ Intertidal, supertidal

HABITAT ~ Rocks

FEEDING HABIT ~ Herbivore

OPERCULUM ~ Corneous

Tectarius pagodus is the largest species in the genus *Tectarius*, which includes many of the largest species within the family Littorinidae. Like all littorinids, *T. pagodus* is herbivorous, and inhabits the upper reaches of the intertidal zone on rocky shores. Thus, the animals are submerged only infrequently, and are resistant to dessication. Animals are active at night during periods of rainfall or high humidity. Species of *Tectarius* have various reproductive strategies. Most produce either feeding or non-feeding planktonic larvae, but two species retain the eggs in the female's body until they hatch.

The shell of the Pagoda Prickly Winkle is white to cream, largely obscured above the keel by many bands of tan to dark brown. It is covered in fine uneven beaded spiral cords, undulating over pronounced axial ribs from the acute body keel upward. On the shoulders of its tall spire, the ribs terminate in large blunt upturned nodules; below the keel the cords are less fine and white. The aperture is white; the interior is pale tan and lined with wide grooves.

DISTRIBUTION

OPHIOGLOSSOLAMBIS VIOLACEA

VIOLET SPIDER CONCH

(SWAINSON, 1821)

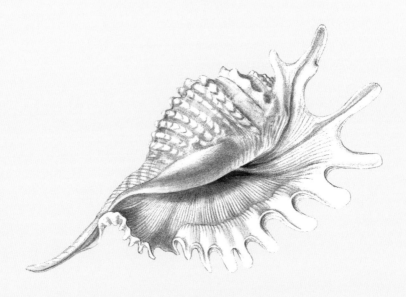

SHELL SIZE RANGE
2¾ to 5¾ in
(70 to 145 mm)

FAMILY ~ Strombidae

DISTRIBUTION ~ Mauritius Islands (western Indian Ocean)

ABUNDANCE ~ Rare

DEPTH ~ 13 to 83 ft (4 to 25 m)

HABITAT ~ Sandy bottoms

FEEDING HABIT ~ Grazer, feeds on filamentous algae

OPERCULUM ~ Corneous, elongated, claw-shaped

Ophioglossolambis violacea is one of the rarest species in the genus, and has a very restricted distribution, found only in Mauritius, in the western Indian Ocean. It is easily recognized by the deep, purple-tinted aperture that gives the shell its name. The color of the aperture seems to be quite stable, since museum specimens more than 100 years old have faded only slightly. There are only about ten species of spider conchs, all of which are restricted to the tropical waters of the Indian and Pacific oceans. They usually live in shallow waters on soft bottoms.

The shell of the Violet Spider Conch is medium in size, thick, and has a broad flared outer lip bearing about 15 to 17 digitations. Such digitations vary in number and size, with those near the posterior end longer than those at or along the anterior end. The spire is long and pointed, and the siphonal canal long and recurved. The dorsal sculpture consists of many strong and nodulose spiral ribs. The shell color is white mottled with brown, the aperture purple, and the broad lip white.

DISTRIBUTION

LISTER'S CONCH

(GRAY, 1852)

SHELL SIZE RANGE
3½ to 6¼ in
(90 to 160 mm)

FAMILY ~ Strombidae

DISTRIBUTION ~ Bay of Bengal and northwestern Indian Ocean

ABUNDANCE ~ Common

DEPTH ~ 165 to 400 ft (50 to 120 m)

HABITAT ~ Sandy bottoms

FEEDING HABIT ~ Herbivore, feeds on algae

OPERCULUM ~ Corneous, elongated, claw-shaped

Mirabilistrombus listeri was once considered one of the rarest shells in collections, and only a few specimens were known until the 1960s, when its habitat was discovered in the northwestern Indian Ocean. It is one of the deepest dwelling strombs, ranging from about 165 to 400 ft (50 to 120 m). *Mirabilistrombus listeri* has a beautifully elegant shell, and its broad flared outer lip has a wide, sinuous stromboid notch near the anterior end.

The shell of the Lister's Conch is of medium size, fusiform, elongated, lightweight but strong, with a high spire and a broadly flared outer lip. The stepped high spire has axial ribs that become obsolete on the last 3 whorls. The body whorl has fine spiral lines and is mostly smooth. The aperture is long and narrow, and the outer lip is flared, with a long, flattened, narrow, posteriorly directed lobe. The shell color is white, covered with yellowish brown zigzag lines. The aperture and outer lip are white.

DISTRIBUTION

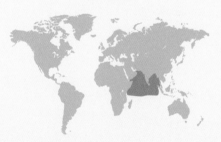

LOBATUS GALLUS

ROOSTER-TAIL CONCH

(LINNAEUS, 1758)

SHELL SIZE RANGE
3 to 7½ in
(75 to 192 mm)

FAMILY ~ Strombidae

DISTRIBUTION ~ Florida to eastern Brazil; West Indies

ABUNDANCE ~ Uncommon

DEPTH ~ 1 to 160 ft (0.3 to 48 m)

HABITAT ~ Sandy bottoms

FEEDING HABIT ~ Herbivore, feeds on algae

OPERCULUM ~ Corneous, elongated, claw-shaped

Lobatus gallus is a distinctive stromb with a large, flared outer lip that has one long projection posteriorly, which recalls a rooster's tail. It is an uncommon species ranging from Florida to eastern Brazil and the West Indies. The term conch usually refers to strombid gastropods, but it is also applied to many unrelated gastropods, usually edible and large, such as species in the families Buccinidae, Melongenidae, and Fasciolariidae. To differentiate them from other groups, the strombids are also known as "true conchs" or strombs. Many strombs are large and edible, and commercial fisheries exist for some species, such as *Lobatus gigas*.

The shell of the Rooster-tail Conch is medium-sized, relatively lightweight, conical, and with a broad, flared outer lip. Its spire is high, with a spiral row of tubercles that become strong knobs on the shoulder of the body whorl; the body whorl has strong spiral threads. The outer lip in adult shells is flared and thickened, with an undulating margin and a long projection posteriorly that extends beyond the spire. The shell color is cream, mottled with orange-tan, and the aperture is pale to golden brown.

DISTRIBUTION

SHINBONE TIBIA

(LINNAEUS, 1758)

SHELL SIZE RANGE
6 to 12½ in
(150 to 310 mm)

FAMILY ~ Strombidae

DISTRIBUTION ~ Japan to Indonesia

ABUNDANCE ~ Common

DEPTH ~ 17 to 500 ft (5 to 150 m)

HABITAT ~ Muddy bottoms

FEEDING HABIT ~ Herbivore, feeds on algae

OPERCULUM ~ Corneous, lanceolate

Tibia fusus is an unmistakable species, with a fusiform shell that has one of the longest siphonal canals among all gastropods. The siphonal canal can be almost as long as the rest of the shell (it varies from about 30 to 45 percent of the shell length). It lives on muddy bottoms, generally in deep water, and is collected by trawling. It is amazing that shells with such a delicate canal are collected from deep water and brought to the surface in perfect condition. *Tibia fusus* has a narrow distribution in the southwest Pacific, and is most common around the Philippines.

The shell of the Shinbone Tibia is long, slender, relatively lightweight, smooth, glossy, and fusiform. Its spire is very tall, with as many as 19 whorls, and an incised suture. The surface of the spire whorls has axial sculpture, but it fades toward the body whorl, which is mostly smooth, with fine spiral lines along its anterior portion. The aperture is lanceolate, the outer lip has 5 long digitations, and an extremely long, straight, or slightly, curved siphonal canal. The shell color is tan to brown, and the aperture white.

DISTRIBUTION

MEDITERRANEAN PELICAN'S FOOT

(MICHAUD, 1828)

SHELL SIZE RANGE
1⅜ to 2½ in
(35 to 60 mm)

FAMILY ~ Aporrhaidae

DISTRIBUTION ~ Norway and Iceland to the Mediterranean

ABUNDANCE ~ Common

DEPTH ~ Offshore to 3,300 ft (1,000 m)

HABITAT ~ Fine mud bottoms

FEEDING HABIT ~ Browser and detritus feeder

OPERCULUM ~ Corneous, elongated

Aporrhais serresianus has the longest digitations among the living species in the family Aporrhaidae. Like other aporrhaids, the shells vary in the number and length of their digitations. The pattern of digitations is important in the identification of the species. These digitations help stabilize the shell on the soft sediment into which aporrhaids burrow. The longer the digitations, the finer the substrate the animal lives on.

The shell of the Mediterranean Pelican's Foot is thin and light, and the flared outer lip has long digitations. The spire is high and the suture well marked. The sculpture consists of 1 spiral beaded row on the spire, and 3 on the body whorl. Typically, there are 4 long digitations that are webbed, and the siphonal canal is also very long. The shell color ranges from white to light brown, and the aperture is white.

DISTRIBUTION

ARESTORIDES ARGUS

EYED COWRIE

(LINNAEUS, 1758)

SHELL SIZE RANGE
1¾ to 4¼ in
(46 to 110 mm)

FAMILY ~ Cypraeidae

DISTRIBUTION ~ East Africa to the central Pacific

ABUNDANCE ~ Common

DEPTH ~ 3 to 33 ft (1 to 10 m)

HABITAT ~ Crevices near coral reefs

FEEDING HABIT ~ Grazer, feeds on algae

OPERCULUM ~ Absent

Arestorides argus has one of the most distinctive shells among the cowries, with dorsal rings or "eyes," and cannot be confused with any other species. It varies considerably in size and in the number of dorsal rings. The species name derives from the character Argus Panoptes from Greek mythology: Argus, said to have 100 eyes, was the "all-seeing" guardian of the heifer-nymph Io. The animal of *A. argus* is dark brown, with a thin mantle that does not obscure the dorsal shell pattern. The mantle has many long, gray-brown branched papillae.

The shell of the Eyed Cowrie is large, cylindrical, heavy, and elongated. The sides are nearly parallel to one another. The aperture is long and narrow, and the apertural teeth long and thin. The apex area is flattened and partially covered by a thick callus. The shell background is beige, and the dorsum has 3 or 4 broad darker bands. The dorsum has brown rings of varying thickness. The base has 4 dark brown blotches.

DISTRIBUTION

MAP COWRIE

(LINNAEUS, 1758)

SHELL SIZE RANGE
2 to 4 in
(50 to 100 mm)

FAMILY ~ Cypraeidae

DISTRIBUTION ~ Indo-West Pacific

ABUNDANCE ~ Common

DEPTH ~ 15 to 120 ft (5 to 35 m)

HABITAT ~ Coral reefs, under corals and stones

FEEDING HABIT ~ Grazer, feeds on algae

OPERCULUM ~ Absent

Cleporicypraea mappa is appropriately named because its dorsum is reminiscent of a worn and burned map. Cowries are glossy because the shell is covered by the mantle; the area on the dorsum where the two lobes of the mantle meet is usually stained in a different color, often as a thin, straight or slightly curved line. In *C. mappa*, this dorsal line is thick and meandering, and sometimes resembles the course of a winding river.

The shell of the Map Cowrie is large for the family, inflated and humped with an ovate outline. Its extremities are thick and the margins callused. The aperture is narrow and long; the teeth do not extend much onto the base, and are sometimes stained in orange. The dorsum is light brown with orange-brown lines and reticulations, with some lighter color spots; the base and extremities are cream. The tan dorsal line is thick, meandering, and outlined in brown.

DISTRIBUTION

TIGER COWRIE

LINNAEUS, 1758

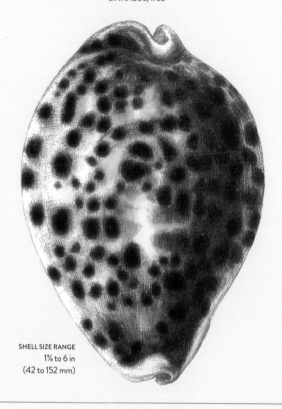

SHELL SIZE RANGE
1⅝ to 6 in
(42 to 152 mm)

FAMILY ~ Cypraeidae

DISTRIBUTION ~ Indo-Pacific, including Hawaii

ABUNDANCE ~ Abundant

DEPTH ~ Shallow subtidal to 60 ft (18 m)

HABITAT ~ Tidepools and rocks near coral reefs

FEEDING HABIT ~ Grazer, feeds on algae

OPERCULUM ~ Absent

Cypraea tigris is one of the best known and arguably one of the most beautiful cowries. It is found in gift shops worldwide and often sold as a "local" shell, although most specimens probably come from the Philippines. *Cypraea tigris* is the type species of the genus *Cypraea* and the family Cypraeidae. It is one of the most variable cowries; no two shells are identical. It also varies widely in size with giant specimens from Hawaii being more than three times larger than the smallest, although both extremes are rare. Unlike most cowries, *C. tigris* usually does not hide in crevices but is commonly found in the open near reefs, and is active during the day.

The shell of the Tiger Cowrie is large, inflated, heavy, smooth, and very glossy. The aperture is narrow, long, and slightly curved, surrounded by thick lips with many strong teeth; columellar teeth extend onto the columella. Shell color and pattern are variable, usually with a white or bluish background and many large, dark irregular spots or blotches often edged with orange-yellow tints. A yellow or orange dorsal line, usually curved, crosses the shell near mid dorsum. The base, aperture, and teeth are white.

DISTRIBUTION

OVULA OVUM

COMMON EGG COWRIE

(LINNAEUS, 1758)

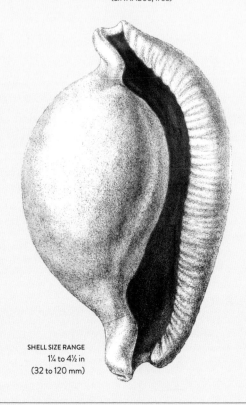

SHELL SIZE RANGE
1¼ to 4½ in
(32 to 120 mm)

FAMILY ~ Ovulidae

DISTRIBUTION ~ Red Sea to Indo-Pacific

ABUNDANCE ~ Common

DEPTH ~ Intertidal to 65 ft (20 m)

HABITAT ~ On soft corals (several species)

FEEDING HABIT ~ Parasitic on soft corals

OPERCULUM ~ Absent

Ovula ovum is the largest ovulid in terms of animal size, although other species, such as *Volva volva* (Linnaeus, 1758) can have longer shells. Both words in the scientific name refer to "egg," which is a good description of its shiny, white egg-shaped shell. The shell is used for decoration as well as for tribal symbols in Melanesia and Polynesia. The animal is jet black, and the velvety mantle has small, white raised spots. It feeds on several species of soft corals. Like many ovulids, *Ovula ovum* resembles true cowries (family Cypraeidae); many ovulid species were originally classified as cypraeids.

The shell of the Common Egg Cowrie is large (for the family), thick, heavy, glossy, inflated, and egg-shaped. Its extremities are elongated, with the anterior one broader than the posterior. The surface is smooth and glossy. The aperture is narrow and long, and widest anteriorly; the outer lip is folded toward the aperture, and irregularly crenulated. The columella is smooth and curved. The shell color is porcelain white, and the interior is red-brown.

DISTRIBUTION

SOLANDER'S TRIVIA

(GRAY, 1832)

SHELL SIZE RANGE
⅜ to ⅞ in
(10 to 21 mm)

FAMILY ~ Triviidae

DISTRIBUTION ~ California to Peru, and Galápagos Islands

ABUNDANCE ~ Common

DEPTH ~ Intertidal to 115 ft (35 m)

HABITAT ~ Rocky bottoms

FEEDING HABIT ~ Carnivore, feeds on ascidians

OPERCULUM ~ Absent

Pusula solandri is one of the largest triviids from the eastern Pacific. It is common under rocks in shallow waters in the southern part of its distribution, and less common in the north. This species has a brownish mantle, peppered with small black and white spots, and short fingerlike, orange-brown papillae. The mantle coloration and texture may provide camouflage when the gastropod is on its colonial ascidian prey. The animal also has a large siphon and short cephalic tentacles, with an eye on a swollen tubercle at the base of each tentacle.

The shell of the Solander's Trivia is large for the family, solid, ribbed, and oval in outline. Its spire is hidden in adult shells by the large body whorl. The sculpture consists of about 11 to 14 strong, continuous ribs. The ribs have rounded nodules along the dorsal groove. The aperture is narrow, widest anteriorly, and both outer and inner lips are denticulate. The shell color is brown to reddish-brown, with 2 dark bands along the dorsum; the ribs and aperture are whitish.

DISTRIBUTION

NATICARIUS CANRENA

COLORFUL ATLANTIC MOON

(LINNAEUS, 1758)

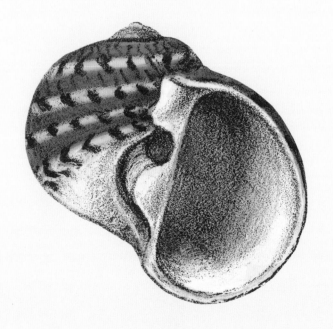

SHELL SIZE RANGE
⅞ to 2½ in
(22 to 65 mm)

FAMILY ~ Naticidae

DISTRIBUTION ~ North Carolina to Brazil, Caribbean

ABUNDANCE ~ Common

DEPTH ~ Offshore to 200 ft (60 m)

HABITAT ~ Sand

FEEDING HABIT ~ Carnivore

OPERCULUM ~ Calcareous, paucispiral

Naticarius canrena is a large, colorful naticid that is popular with shell collectors. The animal is nearly four times the length of the shell, and has a conspicuous mottled pattern on the sides and rear of the foot as well as a propodium with multiple parallel lines. Its operculum is thick, white, and calcified, with a complex pattern of about ten parallel grooves.

The shell of the Colorful Atlantic Moon is smooth, glossy, and roughly spherical, with a rounded spire and a large, D-shaped aperture. The umbilicus is broad, with a broad callus along the midline of the columella. The shell has a complex pattern of narrow white bands on a chestnut brown background, crossed by wavy, dark brown axial lines.

DISTRIBUTION

BUFONARIA FOLIATA

FRILLED FROG SHELL

(BRODERIP, 1825)

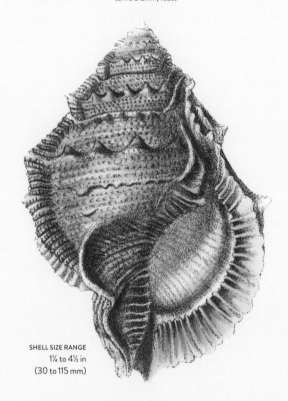

SHELL SIZE RANGE
1¼ to 4½ in
(30 to 115 mm)

FAMILY ~ Bursidae

DISTRIBUTION ~ Somalia to South Africa, and western Indian Ocean

ABUNDANCE ~ Uncommon

DEPTH ~ 85 to 100 ft (25 to 30 m)

HABITAT ~ Rocky and muddy bottoms

FEEDING HABIT ~ Carnivore, feeds on polychaetes

OPERCULUM ~ Corneous, oval

Bufonaria foliata is one of the most striking bursids because of its wide, denticulate, reflected outer lip and columella stained in bright orange-red, which contrast with the normally pale shell. Its varices are separated by about 180 degrees and each lines up with a varix from the previous whorl. It is a rare species in South Africa, where it lives offshore, but may be more common elsewhere. Some species of bursids are known to display sexual dimorphism of apertural features, with egg-laying females having a more flared aperture than non-breeding females or males.

The shell of the Frilled Frog Shell is medium-sized, relatively thin, compressed, and ovate. Its spire is moderately short, with a pointed apex. Several spiral cords bear tubercles, with stronger and pointed spines along the shoulder. The aperture is lanceolate, with a denticulate outer lip, and a wide, lirate columellar shield. The posterior part of the aperture has a long anal canal. The shell color is usually cream or tan, sometimes pinkish, with the periphery of the aperture brightly colored in orange-red.

DISTRIBUTION

CASSIS MADAGASCARIENSIS SPINELLA

CLENCH'S HELMET

CLENCH, 1944

SHELL SIZE RANGE
8 to 16¼ in
(200 to 410 mm)

FAMILY ~ Cassidae

DISTRIBUTION ~ Southeastern U.S.A. to Barbados and
Gulf of Mexico

ABUNDANCE ~ Common

DEPTH ~ 10 to 90 ft (3 to 27 m)

HABITAT ~ Sand and seagrass

FEEDING HABIT ~ Carnivore, feeds on echinoderms

OPERCULUM ~ Corneous, very elongate

Cassis madagascariensis spinella is the largest of the helmet shells. It is a fairly common species in shallow seagrass meadows of the southeastern U.S.A., the Gulf of Mexico, and the Antilles. Its shell is a favorite material to carve for relief-shell cameos and brooches. The artist uses the differently colored shell layers to produce intricate designs. Helmet shells feed on echinoderms such as sea urchins and sand dollars.

The shell of the Clench's Helmet is very large and solid. It appears inflated and has a thick, expanded parietal shield that is ovately triangular in outline. Its spire is short, with thick axial varices spaced three-quarters of a whorl apart. The shell surface has 3 rows of low, rounded knobs, the most prominent at the shoulder, and numerous weaker spiral cords crossed by axial lines. The aperture is long, narrow, and constricted by the thickened outer lip with large teeth. The shell is white or cream in color, with the aperture and parietal shield a glossy, orange tan, with dark brown streaks between the teeth.

DISTRIBUTION

FICUS GRACILIS

GRACEFUL FIG SHELL

(SOWERBY I, 1825)

SHELL SIZE RANGE
3¼ to 8 in
(80 to 200 mm)

FAMILY ~ Ficidae

DISTRIBUTION ~ Indo-West Pacific

ABUNDANCE ~ Common

DEPTH ~ Shallow subtidal to 665 ft (200 m)

HABITAT ~ Sand or mud bottoms

FEEDING HABIT ~ Carnivore, feeds on invertebrates

OPERCULUM ~ Absent

Ficus gracilis has the largest shell in the family Ficidae. It lives in sandy or muddy bottoms in tropical and warm waters at continental shelf depths. The animal has a large arrowhead-shaped foot, and a very long proboscis used to hunt for tube-dwelling worms. Two flaps of tissue cover parts of the shell when the animal is expanded. Like other fig shells, shell shape, sculpture, and coloration do not vary much, and most species have similar shells. The Ficidae are a small family, with only about a dozen recognized species worldwide.

The shell of the Graceful Fig Shell is elongate, thin, fragile, and fig-shaped. Its spire is low, and the suture is deeply impressed. The body whorl is large and inflated, with a wide, long aperture and a long, tapering, slender siphonal canal. The sculpture is fine, with strong low spiral ribs crossed by fine axial lines. The outer lip is thickened at the top. The shell coloration ranges from orange to light brown, with faint, vertical zigzag markings. The aperture can be rich brown to orangish, fading to off-white at the margin of the aperture.

DISTRIBUTION

COMMON DISTORSIO

(LINNAEUS, 1758)

SHELL SIZE RANGE
1⅜ to 4 in
(33 to 100 mm)

FAMILY ~ Personidae

DISTRIBUTION ~ Indo-Pacific

ABUNDANCE ~ Uncommon

DEPTH ~ Intertidal to 100 ft (30 m)

HABITAT ~ Under coral

FEEDING HABIT ~ Carnivore

OPERCULUM ~ Corneous, thin, small

Distorsio anus has one of the largest, most distorted, and most colorful shells in the family Personidae. The animal is very colorful, red or orange, with irregular white blotches, and a pair of small black eyes at the base of long tentacles. It uses its extremely long proboscis to reach into crevices in search of its polychaete prey. The genus name is a good descriptor of the shells of personids, most of which are moderately to severely distorted. There are about 20 living species in the family Personidae worldwide.

The shell of the Common Distorsio is large for the family, inflated, distorted, and fusiform. Its spire is moderately tall, with a pointed apex and a wavering suture. The surface has spiral and axial ribs forming a rough knobby sculpture. The aperture is narrow and constricted, the outer lip thickened, with about 7 teeth, and the columella has strong teeth. There is a broad apertural shield with sharp, meandering edges. The shell color is cream with brown bands.

DISTRIBUTION

CYMATIUM FEMORALE

ANGULAR TRITON

(LINNAEUS, 1758)

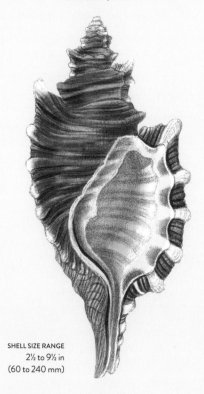

SHELL SIZE RANGE
2½ to 9½ in
(60 to 240 mm)

FAMILY ~ Cymatiidae

DISTRIBUTION ~ Florida to southeastern Brazil

ABUNDANCE ~ Common

DEPTH ~ 2 to 500 ft (0.6 to 150 m)

HABITAT ~ Sandy bottoms near seagrasses

FEEDING HABIT ~ Carnivore, feeds on invertebrates

OPERCULUM ~ Corneous, thick, elongate

Cymatium femorale is a large cymatiid or triton with a distinctive angular, nearly triangular profile. It has two strong, winged varices per whorl; when viewed from the apex, the shell has a triangular profile. *Cymatium femorale* lives on rubble bottoms and near eelgrass beds, ranging from shallow subtidal waters to offshore depths. Young shells are usually more brightly colored than adults. Like other cymatiids, it is a carnivore, and feeds on other mollusks, sea-cucumbers (holothurians), and tube worms.

The shell of the Angular Triton is large, thick, solid, angular, and nearly triangular in outline. Its spire is moderately tall, with angular whorls, a well-marked suture, and a long and narrow apex that is often missing in adults. The sculpture consists of several strong nodulose spiral ribs, with smaller ones between them. The aperture is long and wide, the outer lip is thickened and toothed in adults; the varices are thick and upturned. The siphonal canal is long and recurved. The shell color is reddish brown, with white nodules on the varices, and the interior is white.

DISTRIBUTION

TRUMPET TRITON

(LINNAEUS, 1758)

SHELL SIZE RANGE
4 to 20 in
(100 to 490 mm)

FAMILY ~ Charoniidae

DISTRIBUTION ~ Indo-Pacific; Galápagos Islands

ABUNDANCE ~ Common locally

DEPTH ~ Intertidal to 100 ft (30 m)

HABITAT ~ Coral reefs

FEEDING HABIT ~ Carnivore, feeds on echinoderms

OPERCULUM ~ Corneous, concentric, oval

Charonia tritonis is the largest species in the family Charoniidae. It has been collected for centuries for food, as well as for its beautiful shell. In many areas it has been used as a trumpet, by having a hole drilled into the early whorls. *Charonia tritonis* lives near coral reefs in shallow, tropical waters nearly worldwide. It is a voracious predator, feeding on echinoderms. It is well known as one of the few predators of the large, coral-eating Crown-of-Thorns starfish, *Acanthaster planci*, which can grow to 3 ft (1 m) in diameter.

The shell of the Trumpet Triton is very large, with a high and pointed spire, and an inflated body whorl. The ovate aperture is large, almost half the shell length, with a flared outer lip bearing well-defined teeth. The thickened lip forms an axial ridge that repeats every two-thirds of a whorl, so the varices of every other whorl align. The whorls are rounded and have coarse spiral cords with a single narrow cord between adjacent broad cords. The columella is thick and strongly lirate. The shell color is cream with brown crescents and blotches, the aperture is orange, and the inner lip is white, with brown bands.

DISTRIBUTION

MALEA RINGENS

GRINNING TUN

(SWAINSON, 1822)

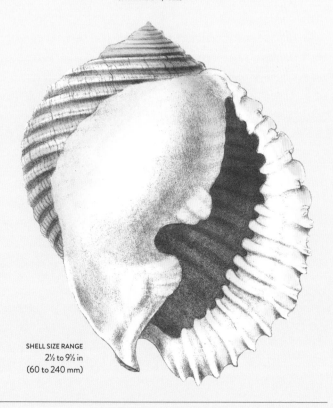

SHELL SIZE RANGE
2½ to 9½ in
(60 to 240 mm)

FAMILY ~ Tonnidae

DISTRIBUTION ~ West Mexico to Peru; Galápagos Islands

ABUNDANCE ~ Common

DEPTH ~ Intertidal to 175 ft (55 m)

HABITAT ~ Sand bars or under rocky ledges

FEEDING HABIT ~ Carnivore, feeds on echinoderms

OPERCULUM ~ Absent

Malea ringens has the thickest and heaviest shell, and the thickest outer lip in the family Tonnidae. Most tuns have thin shells, but that does not deter them from being voracious predators of echinoderms. They use sulfuric acid, produced by the salivary glands, to dissolve a hole in the test (shell) of sea urchins and eat them. Other species feed on sea cucumbers.

The shell of the Grinning Tun is large, solid, heavy, and globose. The spire is low and pointed, and the suture is shallow. The body whorl is large, with regularly spaced, broad, flat spiral ribs. The outer lip is reflected and thickened, with a crenulate outer edge and large teeth on the inner margin. The columella has a deep notch at the midpoint, with a few folds above and below it. The siphonal canal is short and curved. The shell color ranges from dirty beige to brown and the aperture is orange.

DISTRIBUTION

EPITONIUM SCALARE

PRECIOUS WENTLETRAP

(LINNAEUS, 1758)

SHELL SIZE RANGE
1 to 2⅞ in
(25 to 72 mm)

FAMILY ~ Epitoniidae

DISTRIBUTION ~ Indo-West Pacific

ABUNDANCE ~ Common

DEPTH ~ 65 to 400 ft (20 to 120 m)

HABITAT ~ Sandy mud bottoms

FEEDING HABIT ~ Parasitic on sea anemones

OPERCULUM ~ Corneous, oval, multispiral

Epitonium scalare is the best known epitoniid, and prized by collectors. Its exquisite shell is unusual in that its whorls are loosely coiled and do not touch each other, but rather only the bladelike axial varices touch the adjacent whorls. The axial ribs are aligned, which means that the number of ribs per whorl is the same in each whorl. Studies suggest that species with few ribs per whorl, such as *E. scalare*, may have a short life.

The shell of the Precious Wentletrap is medium-sized, thin, lightweight, broad, and conical. Its spire is tall, the whorls rounded, and the suture very deep, because the whorls do not touch, but are joined by the axial ribs. The sculpture consists of about 10 to 11 evenly spaced axial ribs per whorl, and smooth interspaces between ribs. The aperture is oval, the outer lip is thickened, and the umbilicus is deep and wide. The shell color is white or beige, with white axial ribs, a white aperture, and a black operculum.

DISTRIBUTION

WAVED GOBLET

(LINNAEUS, 1758)

SHELL SIZE RANGE
¾ to 1¾ in
(20 to 45 mm)

FAMILY ~ Pisaniidae

DISTRIBUTION ~ Western Pacific

ABUNDANCE ~ Abundant

DEPTH ~ Intertidal

HABITAT ~ Under rocks and coral

FEEDING HABIT ~ Scavenging carnivore

OPERCULUM ~ Corneous, oval

Pollia undosa feeds on a varied diet of bivalves, worms, and carrion, all of which are abundant in its choice of habitat—muddy rocks, and the rubble of broken, dead coral. In life it has a thick brown periostracum. Like other buccinids of warmer waters it has a bright colorful appearance; its polar relatives are much duller. The bright apertural margin and the strong spiral cords are particularly typical of goblet shells, which also frequently exhibit strong axial folds.

The shell of the Waved Goblet is solid and fusiform, with a moderately rounded body. It is white to beige, with faint axial folds and well-defined, chestnut to dark brown spiral cords, becoming obsolete at the apex. The spire is tall, with a fine suture. There are dental folds on both outer lip and columella, and a delicate orange edge to the white aperture. The siphonal canal is short and broad.

DISTRIBUTION

LIGHTNING WHELK

(LINNAEUS, 1758)

SHELL SIZE RANGE
2½ to 16 in
(60 to 400 mm)

FAMILY ~ Buccinidae

DISTRIBUTION ~ New Jersey to Gulf of Mexico and Yucatán

ABUNDANCE ~ Common

DEPTH ~ Intertidal to 65 ft (20 m)

HABITAT ~ Estuaries, bays, and oyster reefs

FEEDING HABIT ~ Carnivore, feeds on bivalves

OPERCULUM ~ Corneous, large and unguiculate, concentric

Sinistrofulgur perversum is the state shell of Texas. It is a large edible gastropod common along the eastern and southern coasts of the U.S.A. that has been used as food by Native Americans for thousands of years. Its popular name originates from the lightning-bolt pattern seen in juvenile shells, but the pattern fades in larger shells. *Sinistrofulgur* species were traditionally classified in the family Melongenidae, but recent studies demonstrate they are buccinids. There are only about ten living species of busyconine whelks, although the subfamily has a long and diverse fossil record.

The shell of the Lightning Whelk is heavy, sinistral, and very large. It is pyriform, almost triangular in profile, with a short spire and broad shoulders that may bear large to small spines, knobs, or low tubercles. The aperture is long and to the left of the smooth columella. A large, corneous operculum protects the animal when it is withdrawn into the shell. The siphonal canal is long and tapering. The shell color varies from a light orange-tan with dark brown stripes in juveniles, to light tan or gray in adults.

DISTRIBUTION

COMMON DOVE SHELL

(LINNAEUS, 1758)

SHELL SIZE RANGE
⅜ to 1 in
(10 to 24 mm)

FAMILY ~ Columbellidae

DISTRIBUTION ~ Florida to Brazil and West Indies

ABUNDANCE ~ Abundant

DEPTH ~ Intertidal to 265 ft (80 m)

HABITAT ~ On and under rocks

FEEDING HABIT ~ Herbivore

OPERCULUM ~ Corneous, smaller than aperture

One of the commonest of the Columbellidae, *Columbella mercatoria* is found in large numbers particularly in the Caribbean on the blades of seagrasses. The shell is often overgrown by algae and, when alive, it has a thin periostracum. The wide variations of color and pattern have given rise to a great many synonyms. Unlike most columbellids, which are opportunistic scavengers by night, *C. mercatoria* is a herbivore and feeds on algae.

The shell of the Common Dove Shell is distinguished by fine spiral cords and very fine axial ribs. Its spire is slightly short of medium. The aperture is narrow, the thickened lip and columella both strongly dentate. Although extremely variable both in color and marking, a typical shell is white with orange to dark brown axial stripes or zigzags.

DISTRIBUTION

MELONGENA CORONA

COMMON CROWN CONCH

(GMELIN, 1791)

SHELL SIZE RANGE
1 to 8 in
(25 to 205 mm)

FAMILY ~ Melongenidae

DISTRIBUTION ~ Alabama to northeastern Florida

ABUNDANCE ~ Locally very common

DEPTH ~ Intertidal

HABITAT ~ Mangroves

FEEDING HABIT ~ Carnivore

OPERCULUM ~ Corneous, oval, large

This spectacular shell has a relatively narrow distribution ranging from northeastern Florida, around the Florida peninsula to Mobile Bay, Alabama, but is locally very common in the brackish water of mangrove areas. It is an aggressive predator, attacking clams, oysters, and other bivalves. Although the family Melongenidae is small in number, its 30 or so species are far-flung, occurring on both sides of the tropical and subtropical Indian, Pacific, and Atlantic oceans.

The shell of the Common Crown Conch is bulbous with a medium spire. The suture is well impressed and the whorls angulated, with 2 spiral rows of curved open spines. A further row of spines occurs on the lower half of the body. The shell has faint axial ridges and is usually decorated with spiral bands of variable width and color from light to purplish brown (although all-cream specimens do occur).

DISTRIBUTION

HOMALOCANTHA SCORPIO

SCORPION MUREX

(LINNAEUS, 1758)

SHELL SIZE RANGE
1¼ to 2½ in
(30 to 65 mm)

FAMILY ~ Muricidae

DISTRIBUTION ~ Red Sea to Indo-West Pacific

ABUNDANCE ~ Common

DEPTH ~ Intertidal to 300 ft (90 m)

HABITAT ~ Rocky bottoms

FEEDING HABIT ~ Carnivore, feeds on mollusks and barnacles

OPERCULUM ~ Corneous, with subcentral nucleus

Homalocantha scorpio is a carnivore that feeds on mollusks and barnacles, and is usually found in shallow waters. Its shell is often heavily encrusted with lime and marine growth. Specimens from old collections usually have four spines on the body whorl, in contrast with five in specimens collected recently. Most shells are brown or have brown spines; albino shells are uncommon. The genus includes species with palmately digitate projections, like *H. scorpio*, and non-palmate spines, as in *H. melanomathos*, from western Africa. The earliest representatives of the genus appeared in the early Cretaceous Period.

The shell of the Scorpion Murex is moderately large for the genus, thick, and fusiform. Its spire can be blunt to moderately high, and the suture is wide and deeply excavated. The aperture is subcircular, and the siphonal canal long and straight. There are 6 to 7 varices with 4 or 5 large flattened foliose spines per whorl, and 2 to 3 large spines on the siphonal canal. The shell color can range from white to brown, with spines usually darker, and the interior is light gray or purplish.

DISTRIBUTION

CHICOREUS CERVICORNIS

DEER ANTLER MUREX

(LAMARCK, 1822)

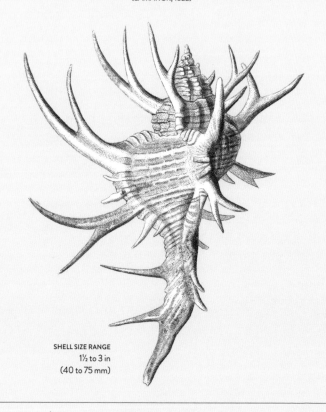

SHELL SIZE RANGE
1½ to 3 in
(40 to 75 mm)

FAMILY ~ Muricidae

DISTRIBUTION ~ Northern Australia, Indonesia, and
Papua New Guinea

ABUNDANCE ~ Common

DEPTH ~ Intertidal to 600 ft (180 m)

HABITAT ~ Rocky bottoms

FEEDING HABIT ~ Carnivore

OPERCULUM ~ Corneous, oval

Chicoreus cervicornis is named for its long spines, which are curved and branched like deer antlers. The longest spines can be as long as the siphonal canal. It is restricted to the northern shore of Australia, Indonesia, and Papua New Guinea. The genus *Chicoreus* is among the most diverse in the family Muricidae, represented by nearly 100 species in tropical waters worldwide; many live in Australia. It is characterized by the presence of three foliaceous or spinose varices per whorl.

The shell of the Deer Antler Murex is medium in size, relatively thin-walled, and fusiform. Its spire is quite high, with an impressed suture, a pointed apex, and rounded whorls. The sculpture is dominated by the 2 long, recurved and branched spines per varix; there are 3 varices per whorl, and several spiral cords. The aperture is white and oval, the outer lip erect and slightly crenulate, and the columella is smooth and curved. The siphonal canal is very long and closed. The shell color ranges from white to pale orange.

DISTRIBUTION

VENUS COMB MUREX

LIGHTFOOT, 1786

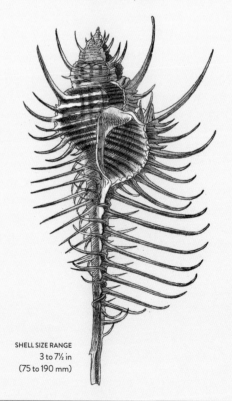

SHELL SIZE RANGE
3 to 7½ in
(75 to 190 mm)

FAMILY ~ Muricidae

DISTRIBUTION ~ Indo-Pacific

ABUNDANCE ~ Common

DEPTH ~ 33 to 165 ft (10 to 50 m)

HABITAT ~ Sandy and muddy bottoms

FEEDING HABIT ~ Carnivore

OPERCULUM ~ Corneous, concentric

Murex pecten is the most spectacular of the long-spined murexes, and a collector's favorite. It is a widely distributed species, and common on shallow soft bottoms. However, perfect specimens with intact spines are uncommon. It is the most spinose murex; its shell has more than 100 long and fragile spines, which provide protection to the animal while preventing it from sinking into soft sediments. As the animal grows, the mantle resorbs spines that would otherwise block the aperture, and secretes new ones to allow for shell growth.

The shell of the Venus Comb Murex is large and thin, with a long, straight siphonal canal, and many long, delicate, and evenly spaced, slightly curved spines. There are 3 varices per whorl, each with many closed spines. The spines on the siphonal canal form an angle of about 90 degrees to the canal axis. The siphonal canal is almost completely closed and very long. The shell color is white to light brown, and the aperture is white.

DISTRIBUTION

PINK-MOUTH MUREX

(SWAINSON, 1831)

SHELL SIZE RANGE
1¾ to 6 in
(45 to 153 mm)

FAMILY ~ Muricidae

DISTRIBUTION ~ Gulf of California to Peru

ABUNDANCE ~ Abundant

DEPTH ~ Intertidal to 1,000 ft (300 m)

HABITAT ~ Among rocks in shallow water

FEEDING HABIT ~ Carnivore, feeds on gastropods and bivalves

OPERCULUM ~ Corneous, ovate, multispiral

Hexaplex erythrostomus is a large and globose muricid that once was the most abundant large gastropod in the Gulf of California. However, due to overharvesting, it is now far less common, and restricted to subtidal depths. It is often collected by shrimp trawlers. It has four or five varices per whorl.

The shell of the Pink-mouth Murex is moderately large for the genus, thick, solid, heavy, and globose-ovate. Its spire is low, the apex pointed, and the suture obscured by the succeeding whorl. The outer surface is rough, with axial varices with open and closed spines, and a smooth, glossy interior. The aperture is large and ovate, and the outer lip crenulate. The columella is smooth, and the siphonal canal large and closed. The shell color is white or creamy pink, and the interior is rich pink.

DISTRIBUTION

SYRINX ARUANUS

AUSTRALIAN TRUMPET

(LINNAEUS, 1758)

SHELL SIZE RANGE
12 to 40 in
(300 to 1,000 mm)

FAMILY ~ Turbinellidae

DISTRIBUTION ~ Northern Australia and Papua New Guinea

ABUNDANCE ~ Common

DEPTH ~ Intertidal to 130 ft (40 m)

HABITAT ~ Intertidal sand flats

FEEDING HABIT ~ Carnivore, feeds on large polychaete worms

OPERCULUM ~ Corneous, with terminal nucleus

Syrinx aruanus is the world's largest shelled gastropod. It is a fairly common species in shallow tidal flats, but also occurs to depths of 130 ft (40 m) off northern Australia and Papua New Guinea. Like other turbinellids, it feeds on tube-dwelling polychaetes. The shell is heavy and voluminous. It is covered with a thick brown skin, the periostracum, that flakes off in empty shells. This gastropod is fished for its meat and shell, which is used to carry water or as a trumpet. Because of the ease in collecting this species, some local populations have declined, causing concern about its conservation.

The shell of the Australian Trumpet is very large and fusiform with a long and straight anterior canal. The aperture and columella are smooth, and the umbilicus deep and elongated, covered partially by a columellar shield. Shells from northern Australia usually are strongly keeled, while those from Western Australia have rounded shoulders. The embryonic shell is quite long, with many whorls and persists in some juvenile shells, although it often erodes away in larger specimens. The shell color is apricot or cream and the aperture is pale yellow to orange.

DISTRIBUTION

ZEBRA VOLUTE

(LEACH, 1814)

SHELL SIZE RANGE
1 to 2¾ in
(25 to 70 mm)

FAMILY ~ Volutidae

DISTRIBUTION ~ Australia, from Queensland to New South Wales

ABUNDANCE ~ Common

DEPTH ~ Intertidal to 180 ft (55 m)

HABITAT ~ Sandy bottoms

FEEDING HABIT ~ Carnivore

OPERCULUM ~ Absent

Amoria zebra, like all species in the genus, is endemic to Australia, ranging from Queensland to New South Wales. It lives on sandy bottoms, from the intertidal zone to offshore. It is a carnivore like other volutes, feeding on other mollusks. This species can sometimes be found in large colonies. Although considered common, *A. zebra* and other *Amoria* species were included on a list of Australian species potentially vulnerable to the shell trade because they can be easily collected in large numbers.

The shell of the Zebra Volute is small for the family, glossy, oblong-ovate, and with a short spire. The protoconch is blunt and rounded, with slightly concave spire whorls and an indented suture. The spire whorls may have axial ribs but the rest of the shell is smooth and glossy. Its body whorl is large and inflated at the shoulder. The outer lip is thickened and the columella has 4 strong folds. The shell color is white to light brown, sometimes golden, with brown axial lines. The aperture and columella are white.

DISTRIBUTION

JUNONIA

(LAMARCK, 1804)

SHELL SIZE RANGE
2½ to 6 in
(64 to 155 mm)

FAMILY ~ Volutidae

DISTRIBUTION ~ North Carolina to the Florida Keys, Gulf of Mexico

ABUNDANCE ~ Uncommon; perfect shells rare

DEPTH ~ 65 to 300 ft (20 to 90 m)

HABITAT ~ Sandy bottoms

FEEDING HABIT ~ Carnivore, feeds on other mollusks

OPERCULUM ~ Absent

In the nineteenth century, *Scaphella junonia* was considered one of the rarest of volutes. This species is now encountered as a bycatch of shrimp boats, making it among the most common of *Scaphella* species. Perfect specimens are still rare, as most shells have healed growth scars. This mollusk lives on sand offshore from North Carolina to the Florida Keys and in the Gulf of Mexico. Like all volutes, it is a carnivore and feeds on other mollusks.

The shell of the Junonia is fusiform, solid, and large. The spire is high, with well-impressed suture and the protoconch is smooth with 1½ to 2 whorls. The teleoconch has 5 whorls, finely sculptured with axial ribs, with the last 2 whorls nearly smooth. The shell color ranges from cream to pale yellow with spiral rows of brown rectangular blotches. The long aperture is pinkish and has 4 columellar folds; the columella and aperture are cream.

DISTRIBUTION

TENT OLIVE

(LINNAEUS, 1758)

SHELL SIZE RANGE
2 to 5 in
(50 to 130 mm)

FAMILY ~ Olividae

DISTRIBUTION ~ Baja California, Mexico to Peru

ABUNDANCE ~ Uncommon

DEPTH ~ Intertidal to 80 ft (25 m)

HABITAT ~ Sandy bottoms

FEEDING HABIT ~ Carnivore, feeds on other mollusks

OPERCULUM ~ Absent

Oliva porphyria has the largest shell in the family Olividae, and one of the most distinctive. It is an uncommon species living in tropical west America, from the intertidal zone to shallow subtidal sandy bottoms. The shell is highly polished by the lobes of its large foot, which envelops the entire shell while the animal burrows through the sand. It is a predator of other mollusks, usually bivalves or gastropods, and is active at night, burying in the sand during the day. It uses its large muscular foot to hold its prey. There are hundreds of species of Olividae worldwide.

The shell of the Tent Olive is heavy, solid, cylindrical, and inflated. Its spire is short with a sharp protoconch and a narrow, channeled suture. Its body whorl is large and inflated, with a long, narrow aperture. The surface is smooth and glossy. The lip is thick, slightly concave in the middle, and smooth. The columella is thickly callused. The shell has a pale violet-pinkish background with rich, brown tent markings; the aperture is orange to pale yellow.

DISTRIBUTION

VENTRAL HARP

P. FISCHER, 1860

SHELL SIZE RANGE
2 to 5¼ in
(50 to 133 mm)

FAMILY ~ Harpidae

DISTRIBUTION ~ Red Sea and Arabian Gulf, Indian Ocean

ABUNDANCE ~ Common

DEPTH ~ Intertidal

HABITAT ~ Sandy bottoms

FEEDING HABIT ~ Carnivore, feeds on crustaceans

OPERCULUM ~ Absent

Harpa cabriti is one of the largest harps, and a common species in the intertidal sandy bottoms of the Red Sea, Arabian Gulf, and Indian Ocean. It is a predatory gastropod, feeding on small crabs and shrimp, which it captures with its large foot. Harps have the ability to shed the posterior part of their foot when molested, leaving the still-moving piece of tissue behind while the snail escapes. Like many sand-dwelling snails, harps lack an operculum. They have such a small radula that for a long time scientists believed they lacked one.

The shell of the Ventral Harp is medium-sized, thick, heavy, and globose-ovate. The spire is short, with a smooth and glossy violet protoconch and well-impressed suture. The whorls are angular, sharply keeled at the shoulder, with pointed spines at each of the axial ribs. The body whorl is inflated and large, with about 15 strong axial ribs, sharply reflected backward. The columella is smooth. The shell color is tan to pinkish with fine, crescent brown lines between ribs, 3 broad darker spiral bands, and 2 large brown blotches on the columella.

DISTRIBUTION

MITRA MITRA

EPISCOPAL MITER

(LINNAEUS, 1758)

SHELL SIZE RANGE
1½ to 7 in
(40 to 180 mm)

FAMILY ~ Mitridae

DISTRIBUTION ~ Red Sea to Indo-Pacific; Galápagos Islands

ABUNDANCE ~ Common

DEPTH ~ Intertidal to 260 ft (80 m)

HABITAT ~ Sandy bottoms

FEEDING HABIT ~ Carnivore, feeds on sipunculan worms

OPERCULUM ~ Absent

Mitra mitra is the largest species in the family Mitridae, and one of the most widely distributed, ranging from the Red Sea, throughout the Indo-Pacific, to the Galápagos Islands. During the day it stays buried in sand, becoming active at night, when it crawls out of the sand to forage. Like other mitrids, it is believed to feed exclusively on sipunculan worms (peanut worms). *Mitra mitra* has a very long and slender proboscis. Large specimens are used by Pacific islanders as a chiseling tool.

The shell of the Episcopal Miter is large, solid, heavy, smooth, and elongate-ovate in outline. Its spire is tall, with a shallow suture; the spire whorls have spiral grooves, but they fade in later whorls, which are smooth. The aperture is about the same length as the spire. The outer lip is thick, and the lower margin has a finely serrated edge; the columella has 4 to 5 folds. The shell color is white, with spiral rows of squarish orange or reddish blotches, and a white or pale yellow aperture.

DISTRIBUTION

QUEEN VEXILLUM

(GMELIN, 1791)

SHELL SIZE RANGE
2 to 3⅜ in
(50 to 86 mm)

FAMILY ~ Costellariidae

DISTRIBUTION ~ Indo-West Pacific

ABUNDANCE ~ Uncommon

DEPTH ~ Shallow subtidal to 165 ft (50 m)

HABITAT ~ Sandy bottoms near coral reefs

FEEDING HABIT ~ Carnivore

OPERCULUM ~ Absent

Vexillum citrinum has one of the most colorful shells in the family. It is a variable species, and some forms have been described on the basis of coloration. It lives on sandy bottoms, feeding on other gastropods, usually in shallow, subtidal tropical waters. Vexillums were originally classified as Mitridae because of overall shell resemblance. However, differences such as apertural lirations, which the mitrids lack, separate vexillums from miters.

The shell of the Queen Vexillum is slender, thick, and fusiform, with a tall spire. The whorls are angulated and the suture is impressed. The sculpture consists of many broad axial, sharply ridged ribs, crossed by smaller spiral riblets. The aperture is narrow and long, the outer lip straight-sided, and the columella has 5 folds. The siphonal canal is curved dorsally. The shell color varies widely, but consists of combinations of brown, orange, yellow, or white spiral bands, with a white or yellowish aperture.

DISTRIBUTION

TRIANGULAR NUTMEG

(GMELIN, 1791)

SHELL SIZE RANGE
⅞ to 1½ in
(23 to 40 mm)

FAMILY ~ Cancellariidae

DISTRIBUTION ~ Sri Lanka to the Philippines and Australia

ABUNDANCE ~ Uncommon

DEPTH ~ Offshore to 330 ft (100 m)

HABITAT ~ Sandy gravel bottoms

FEEDING HABIT ~ Suctorial feeder

OPERCULUM ~ Absent

Trigonostoma scalare has one of the largest shells in the genus. Its distinctive shape separates it from most species in this diverse family: it has a pagoda-shaped shell with sharply keeled whorls that are flat on top. It is an uncommon species found offshore, and like many cancellariids, it lives in sandy bottoms. The diet of cancellariids is not well known because no gut contents can be readily identified. Adaptations in the alimentary system suggest that they are suctorial feeders. Some cancellariids have a trend toward the loss of the radula.

The shell of the Triangular Nutmeg is large for the genus, spiny, and pagoda-shaped in outline. Its spire is tall and stepped, and the whorls barely touch the preceding whorl. The aperture has the triangular shape that is characteristic of the genus, and the lip is thickened. The umbilicus is deep and wide, with a sharp keel around it. The sculpture consists of axial ribs that become spinose at the shoulder, and spiral riblets. The shell color is white or beige, and the interior of the aperture is light brown.

DISTRIBUTION

JAPANESE WONDER SHELL

ANGAS, 1877

SHELL SIZE RANGE
2¾ to 4½ in
(70 to 120 mm)

FAMILY ~ Conidae

DISTRIBUTION ~ Japan to northwestern Australia

ABUNDANCE ~ Uncommon

DEPTH ~ 200 to 2,000 ft (60 to 600 m)

HABITAT ~ Muddy bottoms

FEEDING HABIT ~ Carnivore, feeds on polychaete worms

OPERCULUM ~ Absent

Thatcheria mirabilis is one of the most distinctive shells in the world. In fact, it is so different from any other shell, that when the single specimen was discovered and described as a new species, many scientists believed it to be a malformed specimen. It took more than half a century before other specimens became available. The shape of this shell is said to have inspired Frank Lloyd Wright in designing the Guggenheim Museum in New York. *Thatcheria mirabilis* is the single species in its genus.

The shell of the Japanese Wonder Shell is thin, lightweight, and angular. Its spire is high and stepped. The protoconch is sculptured with criss-crossing diagonal lines forming diamonds. Its spire whorls are nearly flat, with a deep suture and a sharp keel at the shoulder. Its body whorl is large, narrowing sharply toward the wide siphonal canal. The turrid notch is a wide groove about one-quarter of a whorl long. The aperture is large, about half of the shell length, with a very angular profile and a smooth columella. The shell color is dull yellow, and the aperture and columella are white and glossy.

DISTRIBUTION

MATCHLESS CONE

LINNAEUS, 1767

SHELL SIZE RANGE
1½ to 3 in
(40 to 78 mm)

FAMILY ~ Conidae

DISTRIBUTION ~ Lesser Antilles

ABUNDANCE ~ Uncommon

DEPTH ~ 6 to 165 ft (2 to 50 m)

HABITAT ~ Rocky bottoms

FEEDING HABIT ~ Carnivore, feeds on polychaete worms

OPERCULUM ~ Corneous, with terminal nucleus, rather small

Conus cedonulli was one of the rarest shells in the eighteenth century. Indeed, in 1796 a specimen brought more than six times as much as a painting by Vermeer sold at the same auction. It is still considered rare to uncommon and it is prized by collectors for its beautiful pattern. However, with the advent of scuba diving, it is now found more often. All cone shells are venomous and should be handled with care when alive. The venom of *C. cedonulli* is not fatal to humans but its sting may still be painful. There are more than 800 living species in the genus *Conus*.

The shell of the Matchless Cone is thick and conical, and has a long and narrow aperture, in which the lip is nearly parallel to the columella. The spire is short and stepped, and the body whorl is straight-sided, with sculpture consisting of fine spiral lines that are strongest near the base. The shell is white and decorated with irregular spiral lines, beads, and blotches that may range in color from yellow to orange to brown. The shell pattern is extremely variable, and several subspecies have been named.

DISTRIBUTION

MARBLE CONE

LINNAEUS, 1758

SHELL SIZE RANGE
1¼ to 6 in
(31 to 150 mm)

FAMILY ~ Conidae

DISTRIBUTION ~ Indo-West Pacific

ABUNDANCE ~ Common

DEPTH ~ Intertidal to 165 ft (50 m)

HABITAT ~ Rocky bottoms

FEEDING HABIT ~ Carnivore, feeds on other mollusks

OPERCULUM ~ Corneous, elongate

Conus marmoreus is the type species of the genus *Conus*. It is a well-known species, with a striking black and white shell that makes it easily recognized. It is very variable in pattern, ranging from large white tents (triangles) arranged in diagonal spiral rows, to small and very dense tents; a variation from New Caledonia can have caramel-colored or even pure white shells. It is found from the intertidal zone to offshore, on rocky bottoms and under corals. *Conus marmoreus* feeds on other mollusks. Unlike most cones, it is active during the day.

The shell of the Marble Cone is medium to large in size, heavy, with some gloss, and conical in outline. Its spire is short, with a well-marked suture, and large, rounded tubercles at the shoulder. The body whorl has nearly straight sides, and is only slightly convex posteriorly. The aperture is long, widest anteriorly, with a thick or thin outer lip. The surface is usually smooth, but may have spiral lines anteriorly. The shell color is black with white triangular marks arranged in diagonal spiral rows, and a white aperture.

DISTRIBUTION

DUPLICARIA DUPLICATA

DUPLICATE AUGER

(LINNAEUS, 1758)

SHELL SIZE RANGE
¾ to 3⅝ in
(20 to 93 mm)

FAMILY ~ Terebridae

DISTRIBUTION ~ Red Sea to Indo-West Pacific

ABUNDANCE ~ Common

DEPTH ~ Intertidal to 200 ft (60 m)

HABITAT ~ Sandy bottoms

FEEDING HABIT ~ Carnivore

OPERCULUM ~ Corneous, oval

Duplicaria duplicata has an elegant shell with many broad axial ribs and one spiral groove, thus resulting in two zones, which often have different colors. Its shell varies in sculpture and color. It lives on clean sandy bottoms, but not near seagrasses, and is more common offshore. Despite the fact that there are three main feeding types within the family Terebridae, recent molecular studies suggest that the family is monophyletic, meaning that all species share a common ancestor.

The shell of the Duplicate Auger is medium in size, solid, glossy, and elongately conical. Its spire is tall, with a pointed apex, a grooved suture, and nearly straight sides. The sculpture consists of many broad, but sometimes thin, axial ribs, crossed by a spiral groove below the suture. The axial ribs are elevated in early whorls, but become flat toward the body whorl. The aperture is elongate, the outer lip thin, and the columella has 1 diagonal fold. The shell color can be white, beige, orange, gray, or brown, and may be solid or mottled.

DISTRIBUTION

PYRAMIDELLA TEREBELLUM

TEREBRA PYRAM

(MÜLLER, 1774)

SHELL SIZE RANGE
½ to 2 in
(14 to 50 mm)

FAMILY ~ Pyramidellidae

DISTRIBUTION ~ Indo-West Pacific

ABUNDANCE ~ Uncommon

DEPTH ~ Intertidal to shallow subtidal

HABITAT ~ Sand bays

FEEDING HABIT ~ Parasitic carnivore

OPERCULUM ~ Corneous, oval, paucispiral

All species of *Pyramidellidae* are hermaphrodites, and some produce spermatophores, capsules of spermatozoa transferred from one individual to another. Most are parasites, and their eggs are laid in large masses of jelly outside the shells of their chosen hosts. The larval shells are sinistral—wound counterclockwise—but adults are dextral; this results in heterostrophic nuclear whorls, with the axis of the larval shell forming a considerable angle with the axis of the adult shell.

The shell of the Terebra Pyram is smooth and auger-like, with a very tall spire on a rounded body whorl. Its suture is moderately deep, and the slightly convex spire whorls bear 3 dark brown spiral bands on a white to cream background. There are 4 more brown bands on the body whorl, which are visible through the narrow aperture. The columella shows faint folds.

DISTRIBUTION

WOODY CANOEBUBBLE

(LINNAEUS, 1767)

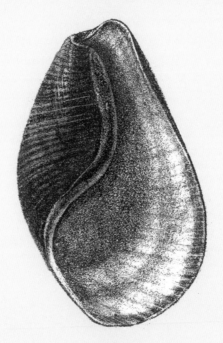

SHELL SIZE RANGE
1¼ to 3 in
(32 to 75 mm)

FAMILY ~ Cylichnidae

DISTRIBUTION ~ Iceland to the Canaries, and the Mediterranean

ABUNDANCE ~ Locally common

DEPTH ~ Shallow subtidal to 2,300 ft (700 m)

HABITAT ~ Sandy bottoms

FEEDING HABIT ~ Carnivore, feeds on bivalves and worms

OPERCULUM ~ Absent

Scaphander lignarius is one of the largest representatives of the family Cylichnidae. The animal burrows in sand as deep as 2 in (50 mm), searching for its prey: bivalves, polychaetes, foraminiferans, and small crustaceans. Like other cylichnids, the animal is too large to withdraw completely into its shell. The flattened head bears no tentacles and has a cephalic shield. The large foot has parapodial lobes used for swimming. The animal has three large, calcified gastric or gizzard plates that are used to grind its food, aided by strong gizzard muscles. Like many other sand-dwellers, there is no operculum. There are about 50 species in the family Cylichnidae worldwide.

The shell of the Woody Canoebubble is thin but sturdy, ovate, and has a sunken spire. The body whorl is greatly expanded anteriorly, narrowing toward the apex. The aperture is as long as the shell and widest anteriorly. The outer lip is thin and extends above the spire. The columella is smooth and curved, with a white parietal shield. The sculpture consists of fine incised spiral lines, crossed by fine growth lines. The shell is tan with a darker periostracum, and white inside.

DISTRIBUTION

CRUSTY NAUTILUS

(LIGHTFOOT, 1786)

SHELL SIZE RANGE
6 to 8½ in
(180 to 215 mm)

FAMILY ~ Nautilidae

DISTRIBUTION ~ New Guinea and Solomon Islands

ABUNDANCE ~ Uncommon

DEPTH ~ 330 to 1,000 ft (100 to 300 m)

HABITAT ~ Water column where coral reefs drop off into deep water

FEEDING HABIT ~ Carnivore, feeds on shrimp, crabs, and fishes

OPERCULUM ~ Absent, but its leathery hood serves a similar function

Allonautilus scrobiculatus is a species of Nautilus with a narrow distribution, living in deep waters off Papua New Guinea to the Solomon Islands. Like other cephalopods, Nautilus species swim by jet propulsion, pumping water through a muscular funnel, the hyponome, which propels the animal backward. The Crusty Nautilus has about 90 tentacles, which it uses to hunt for prey, aided by chemical cues. Like other species of Nautilus, its shell has as many as 30 hollow chambers.

The shell of the Crusty Nautilus is large, planispiral, and has a large, open umbilicus on both sides of the shell. The body whorl has sinusoidal radial folds. The external surface of the shell is dull cream, adorned with thin, straight, radial, and brownish to reddish stripes spanning a quarter to a half of the body whorl. The part adjacent to the aperture is stained in black by the animal. The aperture and chambers are pearly white.

DISTRIBUTION

ARGONAUTA NOURYI

HORNED PAPER NAUTILUS

LOROIS, 1852

SHELL SIZE RANGE
3¼ to 4 in
(80 to 98 mm)

FAMILY ~ Argonautidae

DISTRIBUTION ~ Baja California to Panama

ABUNDANCE ~ Uncommon

DEPTH ~ From near the surface to deep water

HABITAT ~ Oceanic pelagic

FEEDING HABIT ~ Carnivore, feeds on crustaceans and other mollusks

OPERCULUM ~ Absent

Argonauta nouryi is perhaps the rarest of the argonautids. Although it is reminiscent of Nautilus species, its "shell" is not the equivalent of this or any other molluscan shell; it is an evolutionary novelty found only in the family Argonautidae. This egg case is formed by a secretion from the female's two webbed dorsal arms. Like all octopods, it has eight arms. This egg case has two rows of sharp and relatively long tubercles, and hornlike lateral protrusions.

The egg case of the Horned Paper Nautilus is medium-sized, paper-thin, lightweight, fragile, laterally compressed, and discoid in outline. Each side has a pointed and long projection. Its sculpture consists of radial raised ribs; every other rib ends in a sharp tubercle at the periphery of the shell. Internally, the radial ribs show as grooves. The aperture is long and wide, and the outer lip thin. The color is white, and the tubercles are stained in brown in early whorls but fade to white toward the body whorl; the interior is white.

DISTRIBUTION

GLOSSARY

Adductor muscle Muscle joining the two valves of a bivalve mollusk, and closing the shell when contracted.

Anterior (prefix: antero-) The forward portion of the animal, near the head.

Aperture The opening through which the animal extends from the shell, and the most recent part of the shell to be formed.

Apex The first portion of the shell to be formed, situated at the tip of the spire.

Aragonite A crystalline form of calcium carbonate. Mother-of-pearl and nacre are composed of aragonite.

Axial Parallel to the shell axis.

Axis A line passing through the apex around which the whorls of the shell are coiled.

Bead A round raised feature, smaller than a nodule, repeated to form a linear pattern on the surface of a shell resembling a necklace.

Bilateral symmetry A type of symmetry in which the two sides of an animal are mirror images of each other.

Body whorl The last whorl (360 degrees) of a gastropod shell to be deposited.

Byssus Proteinaceous fibers secreted by the foot of a bivalve and used to form a temporary attachment to a hard substrate.

Calcareous Composed of or containing calcium carbonate.

Callus A thickened layer of shell along the parietal or columellar region of the shell.

Canal A channel in the shell that is occupied by an organ of the mollusk, for example, the siphonal or anal canal.

Cephalic Pertaining to the head.

Channel A deep groove, usually following a spiral path, forming part of the interior or exterior surface decoration of a shell.

Chemoautotroph An organism that derives energy from chemical oxidation of inorganic compounds rather than from sunlight.

Chitinous Composed of chitin, a semitransparent, horny substance found in the shells of some mollusks.

Collar A thin ribbonlike exterior surface rib, often with a frilly outer edge, encircling and more or less perpendicular to the shell.

Columella The central pillar of the shell, formed by the inner lip of the aperture around the axis of coiling.

Cord A thick, rounded, continuous sculptural element.

Corneous Made of a hornlike substance such as conchiolin or scleroprotein; not calcareous.

Crenulate With alternating furrows and ridges, which are scalloped or corrugated.

Denticle A single, toothlike projection. A shell with such projections is termed dentate or denticulate.

Deposit feeder A mollusk that feeds on decomposing organic matter deposited on the floor of its habitat, either on the floor surface or by tunneling deep into it.

Dextral Coiled in a clockwise direction when viewed from the apex of a shell; relating to shells with the aperture to the right of the coiling axis.

Digitation A fingerlike projection.

Dorsum (adj: dorsal) The upper side of a mollusk, or of any animal that moves in a horizontal position.

Filter feed To feed on particles or microorganisms filtered from the water.

Fold A spirally wound ridge on the columella of a gastropod.

Foliose Leaflike.

Foramen An opening, hole, or passage through the shell.

Foraminifera A phylum of single-celled micro-organisms with a shell formed of calcium carbonate.

Fusiform Spindle-shaped; swollen in the middle, tapering toward the ends.

Girdle A band of leathery or muscular tissue holding the valves of a chiton in place.

Globose Spherical.

Growth line A line on the shell surface that marked the position of the shell margin during an earlier stage of growth; delineate increments of shell growth.

Hinge Region along the dorsal portion of bivalve shells that allows for limited motion of the two valves relative to each other.

Intertidal The region exposed at low tide and submerged at high tide.

Keel A sharp, raised, blade-like spiral sculptural element. Usually present along the shell periphery or shoulder.

Labrum The outer lip of a coiled shell.

Lamella (adj. lamellose) A thin platelike structure that often occurs in multiples.

Lanceolate Leaf-shaped; narrow and tapering to a point.

Ligament An elastic, structure made of conchiolin, which joins the valves of a bivalve and provides the force to open the valves when the adductor muscles are relaxed.

Lip The margin of the aperture. The inner lip extends from the suture to the base of the columella, and includes the parietal region. The outer lip is the part of the apertural margin farthest from the shell axis. It also extends from the suture to the base of the columella.

Lira (pl. lirae) A narrow, linear ridge along the shell, or within its outer lip.

Mantle The outer portion of a mollusk's body that secretes the shell.

Margin Edge of the shell.

Multispiral With multiple whorls around a central point.

Muscle scar A region on the interior surface of the shell to which a muscle is or was attached.

Nacre An iridescent inner shell layer composed of thin layers of aragonite. Also called mother-of-pearl.

Nodulose Having small knobs or nodules.

Notch An indentation in the shell margin, usually with a V-shaped or U-shaped profile.

Ocelli Multiple, light-sensing eyes, as in the mantle margin of a scallop.

Operculum A circular or elongated structure produced by some gastropods to block or seal the aperture of the shell when the animal withdraws. May be corneous or calcareous.

Ovate Egg-shaped.

Parapodia Lateral extensions of the foot.

Parietal The posterior portion of the inner lip of a gastropod, between the columella and the suture.

Paucispiral Having few whorls around a central point.

Pelagic Living in open ocean waters; free-swimming or floating.

Periostracum A thin organic layer of conchiolin, the sometimes fibrous outer coating of the shell during the life of many mollusks.

Plankton Organisms that drift near the surface of the ocean.

Polychaete A type of worm.

Porcelaneous Having a smooth white surface like fine porcelain.

Posterior (prefix: postero-) The rear portion of the animal; farthest from the head along the axis of the body.

Protoconch Larval shell of a gastropod; that part of the shell formed before the larva undergoes metamorphosis. Situated at the tip of the apex.

Pyriform Pear-shaped.

Radial Extending outward from the center.

Radula A flexible ribbon supporting multiple rows of chitinous teeth. A feeding structure unique to mollusks, but absent in bivalves.

Ray A linear mark of surface color, radiating like a ray of light from a central point such as the apex.

Recurved Curving backward or inward.

Reticulated Having a netlike pattern.

Rib A raised, rounded structure on the shell surface.

Rugose Having a surface with wrinkles and ridges.

Scar A repaired break in the shell.

Selenizone A narrow, conspicuous, parallel-sided band of shell material that runs along the whorls of shells that have a slit. It originates at the back of the slit and has the same width.

Shoulder An angulation in the curvature of the whorl, usually fairly close to the suture.

Siphon A fleshy tube through which water enters the mantle cavity.

Sipunculan A phylum of bilaterally symmetrical unsegmented marine worms.

Spicule A small spike or needlelike structure.

Spinose Having spines.

Spire The portion of the shell between the apex and the body whorl.

Stria A shallow, incised groove in the surface of the shell.

Stromboid notch A sinuous indentation along the outer lip of the shell, near the siphonal canal. Prevalent in the family Strombidae, but also present in other gastropods.

Substrate An underlying layer.

Subtidal Below the low tide line.

Suspension feeder Animals that feed on material that is suspended in the water, usually by straining them from the water; also known as a filter feeder.

Suture A line along the shell surface along which adjacent whorls join.

Symbiont An organism that is the beneficiary of a symbiotic relationship with another organism.

Teleoconch That portion of the shell produced after the larva undergoes metamorphosis; the adult shell.

Terminal Marking or located at the extremity of a given physical or decorative feature.

Tooth Protuberance inside the lip of a gastropod shell, or on the hinge of a bivalve shell.

Trema (plural: tremata) An opening in the shell that allows excretory products to exit.

Tubercle A wartlike projection.

Type species The species that serves as the basis for defining a genus or subgenus.

Umbilicus A hollow, usually conical opening in the base of the shell. Present in shells in which the entire aperture, including its inner edge, is completely outside the coiling axis.

Umbo (plural: umbones) The first part of a bivalve shell to form; the apex of each valve.

Unguiculate Resembling claws.

Valve A distinct, calcified structure that forms all or part of the shell.

Varix (plural: varices) A thickening along a lip of the shell, usually indicating an interruption in growth and reinforcement of the shell edge.

Velum The membrane of the larvae of some species of mollusk, covered in fine cilia whose waving motions aid the larva's movement.

Whorl A complete rotation (360 degrees) of the shell growth around the coiling axis.

INDEX OF SPECIES BY COMMON NAME

INDEX OF SPECIES BY SCIENTIFIC NAME

ACKNOWLEDGMENTS

The illustrations of the shells in this book are mostly derived from the classical iconographies depicting the then known diversity of mollusks that were published during the nineteenth century. These were produced in an era when illustrations were engraved and printed, and then individually colored by hand. We acknowledge the scientific efforts of the authors, who assembled and described these species, many new to science at the time, as well the artistic talents of the engravers, printers, and colorists who produced the images in the following works, on which the illustrations in this book are based.

Sources for the images in this book are:

Chenu, J. C., 1842–1854. *Illustrations Conchyliologiques ou description et figures de toutes les coquilles connues vivantes et fossiles, classées suivant système de Lamarck.* Fortin, Masson & Langlois et Leclercq. Paris. Volumes 1–4. 482 plates (358 colored). Illustrations on the following pages come from various volumes of this series: 30, 34, 36, 38, 40, 44, 46, 48, 50, 54, 76, 108, 126, 144, 146.

Kiener, L. C., 1834–1850. *Spécies Général et Iconographie des Coquilles Vivantes, comprenant la collection du Muséum d'Histoire Naturell de Paris, la collection Lamarck, celle du Prince Masséna et les decouvertes récentes des Voyageurs.* Rousseau/Baillière, Paris. Volumes 1–11. 826 colored plates. Illustrations on the following pages come from various volumes of this series: 68, 70, 72, 74, 78, 94, 96, 102, 112, 124, 130, 132, 136, 152, 156, 158.

Reeve, Lovell, 1843–1878. *Conchologia Iconica, or, Illustrations of the Shells of Molluscous Animals.* Reeve Brothers, London. Volumes 1–20. 2,727 colored plates. Illustrations on the following pages come from various volumes of this series: 22, 24, 26, 28, 32, 56, 58, 62, 64, 66, 80, 82, 84, 88, 90, 92, 100, 106, 110, 114, 116, 118, 122, 128, 138, 140, 142, 148, 150, 160, 164, 166, 168.

Sowerby, G. B. II, 1841. *The Conchological Illustrations.* Sowerby, London. 200 colored plates. The illustration on p. 98 came from this publication.

Sowerby, G. B., 1847–1887. *Thesaurus Conchyliorum, or monographs of the genera of shells.* Sowerby, London. Volumes 1–5. 530 plates. Illustrations on the following pages come from various volumes of this series: 60, 104, 120, 154, 162.

Sowerby, G. B., 1870. Descriptions of Forty-eight new Species of Shells. *Proceedings of the Zoological Society of London for 1870:* 249-259, pls. 21–22. The illustration on p. 86 came from this publication.

Tryon, G. W. (continued by H. A. Pilsbry), 1879–1898. *Manual of Conchology: Structural and Systematic.* Tryon, Philadelphia. First Series, 1–17. Illustrations on the following pages come from various volumes of this series: 20, 134.

Tryon, G. W. 1882–1884. *Structural and Systematic Conchology: an introduction to the study of the Mollusca.* Tryon, Philadelphia. 3 volumes. 140 plates, some colored. The illustration on p. 52 came from this publication.

Wood, W., 1835. *General Conchology; or, A description of Shells arranged according to the Linnean System, and Illustrated with Sixty Plates, containing 260 Figures of Univalves and Bivalves.* John, Booth, London, 246 pp, 60 hand-colored plates. The illustration on p. 42 came from this publication.

M. G. H.